63

# PI-WATER

❁

# The Water of Life

Kirlian photograph of the aura radiated from ceramic embedded with Pi-water information. The black spot in the center is a 5mm-diameter ceramic ball.

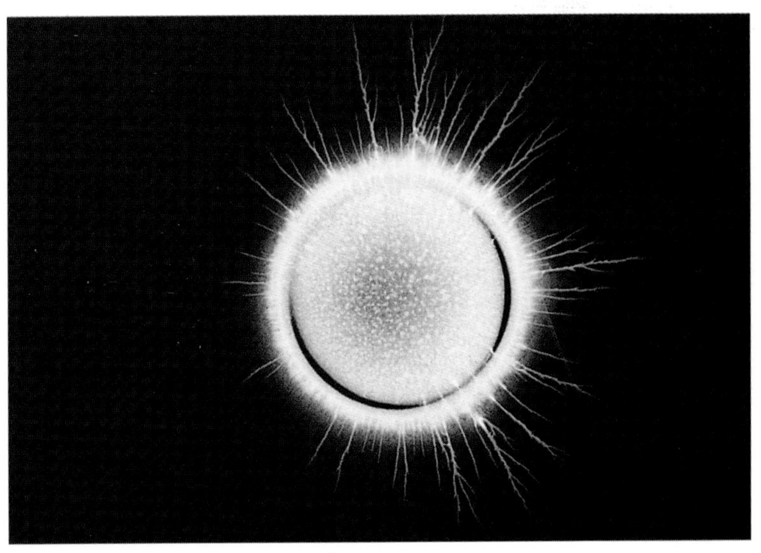

Aura picture of Pi-water in a test tube.

**THIS IS WHAT PI-WATER IS.**

Tuna fish were preserved in 0°C water for 20 days. The gills of fish treated with Pi-water (top) appear fresh.

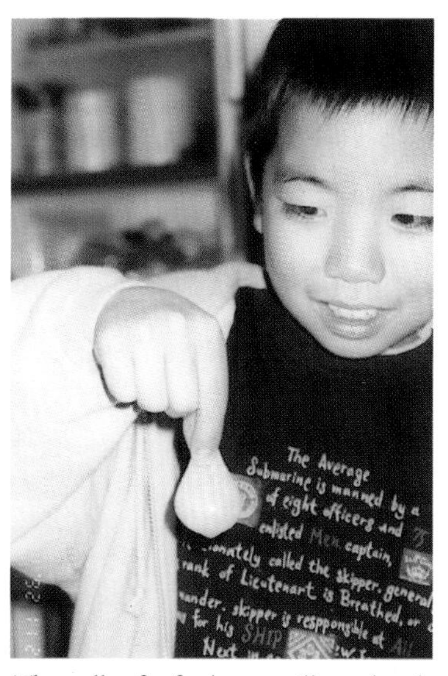

The yolk of a fresh egg will not break when picked up by hand.

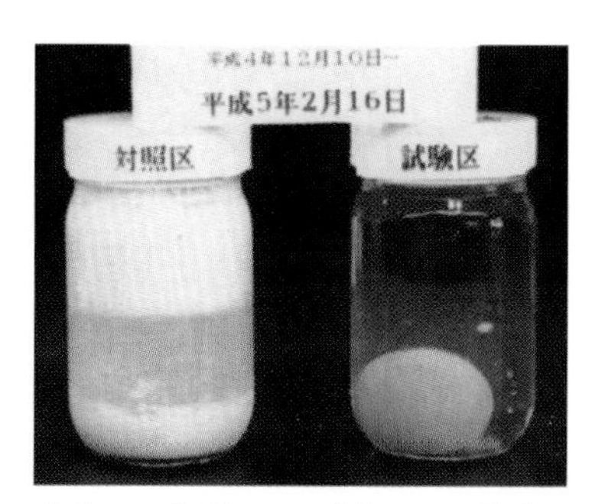


6. An egg in Pi-water did not spoil after two months at room temperature (right). The other egg in untreated water decayed and became milky (left).

Hens in the Inachi poultry farm in Toyohashi City, Japan, are fed Pi-water.

## AMAZING FRESHNESS RETENTION AND POLLUTION-FREE FOODS.

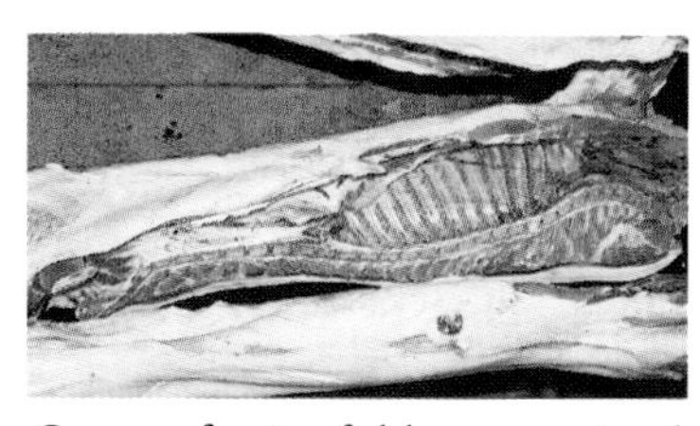

Carcass of swine fed by conventional methods: the meat is blotchy with congested blood.

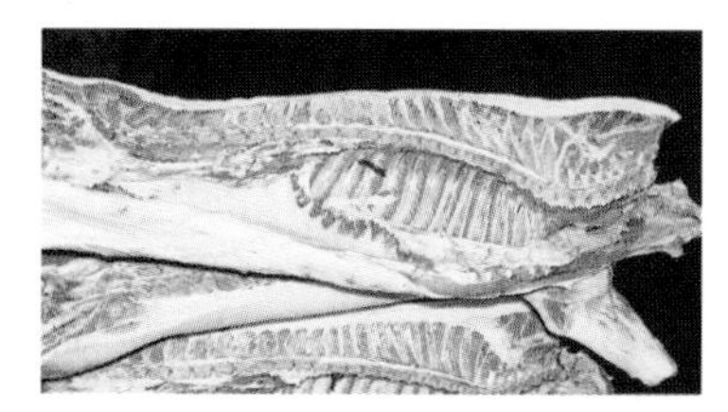

Carcass of swine fed with Pi-water remains edible and tasty for a longer period of time.

The test area (left) was treated with Pi-water soil conditioner and a double amount of nitrogen. The control area (right) was treated in the conventional way.

Nursery boxes of rice plants, showing significant difference in growth of roots in untreated (bottom) and Pi-water-treated (top) sections.

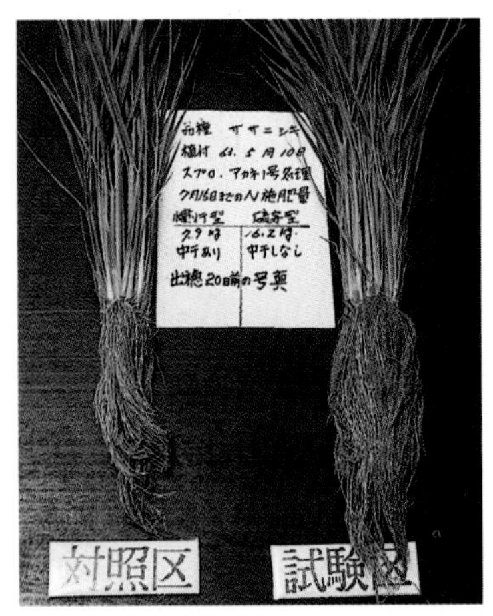


The firm growth of roots is very important. Rice plants on the right were treated with Pi-water and soil conditioner.

Revival of earthworms, pond snails, and leeches.

**HEALTHY GROWTH OF RICE PLANTS WITHOUT AGRICULTURAL CHEMICALS PRODUCES A BETTER HARVEST.**

The cultivation of chemical-free melon is possible.

New sprouts shoot out from decayed dracaenas.

Seed treatment with Pi-water caused a significant difference in potato plants' growth (right).

Clear differences in the growth of hyacinth roots is apparent.

## Amazing growth promoted by Pi-water.

Healthy strawberry plants growing in soil treated with Pi-water soil conditioner.

Under conventional cultivation methods, strawberry field passages fill with water, and plant growth is poor.

Pi-water makes strong, durable concrete in which no cracks occur, thus increasing the life span of buildings.

Concrete is made from alkaline sand, such as andesite; some cracks will occur.

## Pi-water systems in industrial fields.

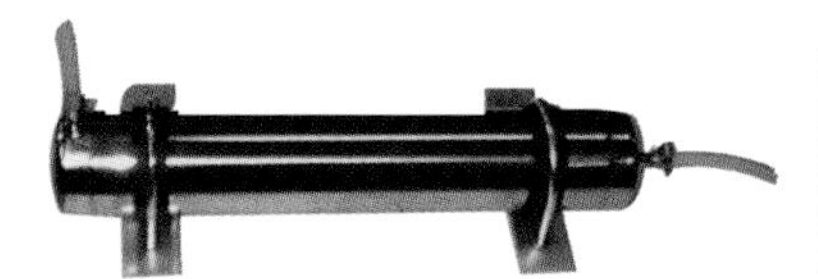

Energy emission control system with Pi-water.

Besides improving fuel efficiency, the Pi-water system decreases a diesel engine's DEP, which is considered a cause of lung cancer.

Large-sized Pi-water processor for industrial use.

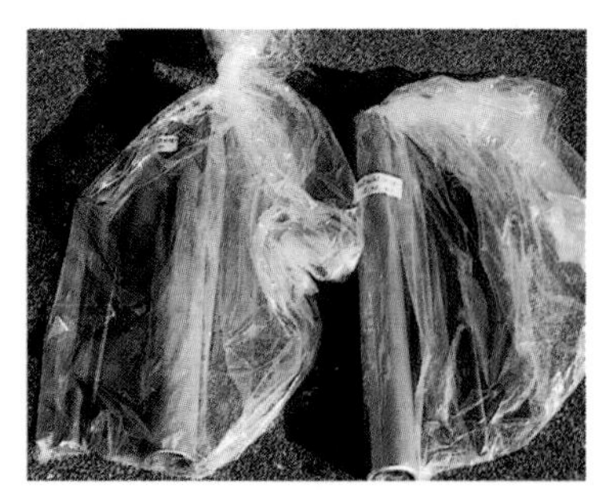

Iron pipe treated with Pi-water will not rust even when placed next to a vinyl bag (right) containing cotton soaked with concentrated hydrochloric acid. Untreated iron pipe (left) will rust quickly.

Carp, a freshwater fish, and sea bream, a seawater fish, can live together in Pi-water-treated water.

The muscle of a rat will not decay after six months in Pi-water (right).

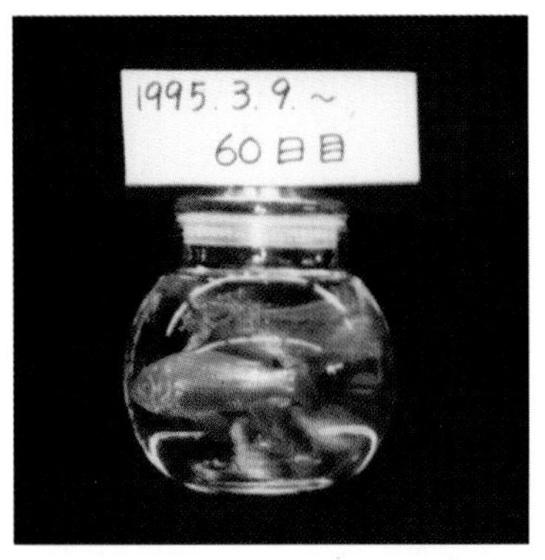


A goldfish can live for five months in a completely sealed jar containing Pi-water.

**THE POWER OF HIGH ENERGY.**

After waste water from a chicken broiler plant is filtered through a Pi-water system, the water will become clear enough for fish to live in.

Mineral water using Pi-water technology.

Cosmetics using Pi-water technology.

## PI-WATER EXTENDS HEALTHY LIFE.

Pi-water purifier.

Healthy marine products in a restaurant's Pi-water tank. The treated water is brighter than other water.

A view of Mikawa Hot Spring in Mikawa Bay quasi-national park, a popular Pi-water spa.

There are excellent views from the windows of the Mikawa Onsen Hotel in Mikawa Bay quasi-national park.

# PI-WATER
# THE WATER OF LIFE

By

Shinji Makino, Ph.D.

*Translated by David Y.S. Kim, M.D., and Kazuko Kuriyama*

IBE COMPANY, LTD.

NAGOYA, JAPAN

*Pi-Water: The Water of Life*

International Standard Book Number: 0-9670571-1-6
Library of Congress Catalog Number: 2002102629



Published originally in Japan

Printed in the United States of America

Deisgned and produced by Kepler Associates, Chicago, Illinois

Cover design by Pi-Tech America, Lincolnwood, Illinois

This book is available for special promotions and premiums.
Please contact the publisher for details.

IBE JAPAN
18-30, Meiekiminami 1-chome, Nakamura-ward
Nagoya, Aichi 450-0003, Japan
Telephone: 81-52-586-3161; Fax: 81-52-541-3830
www.ibe-techno.com

PI-TECH AMERICA, INC.
7300 North Cicero Avenue
Lincolnwood, Illinois 60712 USA
Telephone: 847-675-5151, 847-675–0390; Fax: 847-763-8012

# TABLE OF CONTENTS

# LIST OF ILLUSTRATIONS

# PROLOGUE

❁ ❁ ❁

# THE CIRCUMSTANCES SURROUNDING OUR HEALTH

## CONTINUING ENVIRONMENTAL POLLUTION

I feel it would be no exaggeration to say that global environmental pollution shows no sign of abating. We are beset by problems, such as the destruction of the ozone layer by Freon gas and the problems of trihalomethanes and dioxin, not to mention the threat of nuclear pollution. On top of that, we have pollution caused by supermicroscopic environmental hormones.

We have a situation where not only human life but all life on earth is under threat. If we take just illnesses that specifically affect human life, we find pollinosis (hay fever), O-157, the appearance of antibiotic resistant MRSA, and declining sperm counts, thought to be attributable to environmental endocrine disruptors (EED). None of these things was even dreamed of a few decades ago, and the list goes on.

I would like to take Freon gas as an example here. When it was first developed, it was lauded as a "dream substance," the "fruit of man's wisdom." It was then used not only as the cooling agent in freezers and air-conditioning systems but also in a number of other applications such as in the washing process for IC chips.

Not only was it good for many useful applications, but also, being extremely stable, it was completely harmless to human beings. Moreover, if you disposed of it, it just evaporated as gas. It couldn't have been more convenient. However, the rejoicing was to be short-lived. As the discarded Freon gas reached the upper layers of the earth's atmosphere, it began to destroy the ozone layer, thus adding to the Greenhouse Effect.

Most of the strong ultraviolet light emitted by the sun is absorbed by the ozone layer. Therefore, only a small amount actually reaches the earth itself. Thanks to this ozone layer, life on earth, both animal and vegetable, is able to live comfortably.

However, now this ozone layer is being destroyed with a large hole appearing in it. Already they say that, because of this hole's covering an area stretching from the South Pole to Australia, it is compulsory for the children of that country to wear sunglasses and a hat to protect themselves from ultraviolet sunlight.

Moreover, even more troubling is the fact that Freon gas rises very slowly, taking some 15 years to reach the ozone layer. Thus, the Freon gas destroying the ozone layer now was released some 15 years ago. Therefore, even if we were to ban the disposal of Freon today, the destruction of the ozone layer would continue for another 15 years, and the hole in the ozone layer would continue to widen apace. This is a truly worrying development.

Let's look at another example. It would not be too much to say that our daily lives have become dependent on plastic. It is extremely convenient. Things such as buckets and tableware made of plastic are light but neither break nor wear. Moreover, it couldn't be easier to process. Because it has such an excellent range of applications, it is used in every aspect of our lives. Everything from tableware and buckets to plumbing pipes, car seats, automobile parts, and construction materials—even paint and clothing.

However, with plastic, too, there is a number of worrying problems. For one, when it is disposed of and incinerated, it produces the highly poisonous substance dioxin. Large amounts of dioxin have already been found in the milk of mothers living near such incineration sites.

It has been confirmed that environmental endocrine disruptors (EED) are produced by tableware made of polycarbonate. It is known that EED, being supermicroscopic, impair the ability of humans and life in general to reproduce. It is said that certain species of shellfish have declined markedly because of these disruptors. Recently, the birthrate in Japan has shown a conspicuous decline. It is possible that such EED have played a part in this.

I have given the two examples of Freon and plastic. However, these represent only one small fraction of the problems human beings now face—problems too numerous to mention.

If we really look closely at these problems, it becomes clear that they are due to man's continual production of chemicals that do not naturally exist in nature. These kinds of substances never fail to cause a problem somewhere in the natural cycle. I can't help feeling that, somehow, God is having a laugh at man's short-sighted intelligence.

If we compare global pollution with that of the past (1965-85), we can see that, thanks to much effort on behalf of many people, things have improved greatly in many ways. Even so, I feel that we still have a long way to go.

Global pollution affects the health of each and every human. We have atopic dermatitis, pollinosis, asthma, 0-157, and MRSA , not to mention AIDS and Ebola. And the list of illnesses that didn't exist before goes on. I feel this is all due to man upsetting the natural wisdom of nature. Even though it may be a little inconvenient, I wonder if the best solution would be to adjust our lifestyle to fit in with the wisdom of Mother Nature.

### MEDICAL TREATMENT: A LOOK AT THE DYNAMICS OF PATIENT NUMBERS AND THEIR SIGNIFICANCE

Let's look at the figure, Trends in Treatment by Type of Injury or Complaint. This gives us a dynamic picture of trends in various types of illness or injury. This is quoted from statistics produced by the Ministry of Welfare. Surprisingly, the number of patients for nearly all types of complaint can be seen to be rising year by year.

So what do these statistics show us? Medicine continues to progress day by day. But even so, the sick continue to show a marked increase in number. To put it simply, as medicine progresses and cures are found, we should be able to see a decline in patient numbers year by year.

Looked at in another way, even though medicine has made great strides, it would appear that for a number of chronic diseases it has yet to find a decisive cure.

Cancer, diabetes, liver complaints, all of them remain unconquered.

If we look at this graph in detail, the picture becomes very clear. For example, if we look at diseases related to high blood

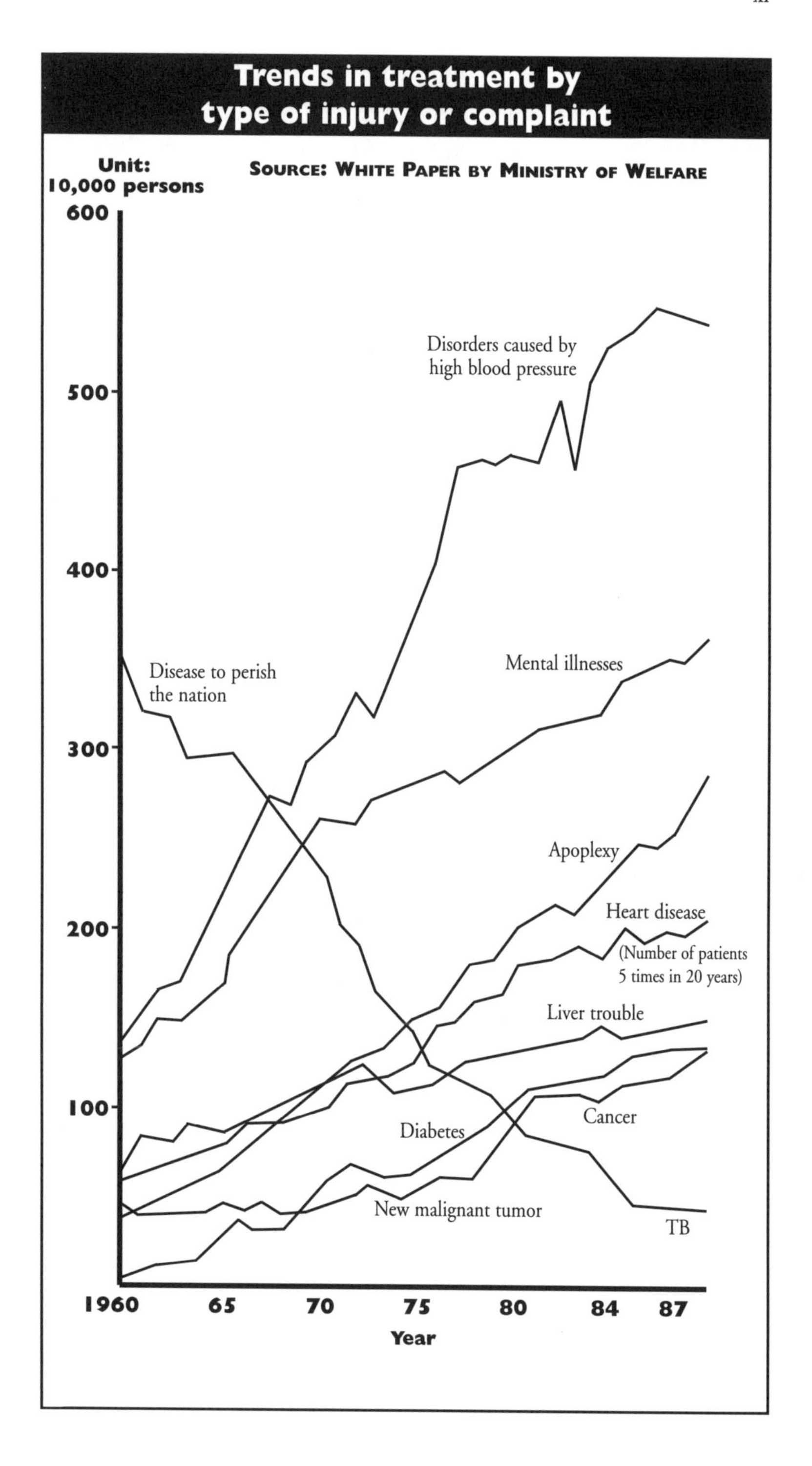
Trends in treatment by type of injury or complaint
Unit: 10,000 persons
SOURCE: WHITE PAPER BY MINISTRY OF WELFARE
600
500
400
300
200
100
Disorders caused by high blood pressure
Disease to perish the nation
Mental illnesses
Apoplexy
Heart disease
(Number of patients 5 times in 20 years)
Liver trouble
Diabetes
Cancer
New malignant tumor
TB
1960
65
70
75
80
84
87
Year

pressure, we find that although drugs to alleviate it are available, we find that blood pressure drops while the patient is under medication only to go up when treatment is withdrawn. This can by no means be considered a cure. The symptoms have merely been suppressed. Because of this, patient statistics show a rapid increase.

Next, if we take diabetes as an example, in 1987 the number of sufferers was between 1,200,000 and 1,300,000. However, today, more than ten years later, their number has increased drastically and is now between 5 to 6 million. Moreover, this is only the figure for those receiving treatment at a hospital. One in ten adults over the age of 40 is diabetic. Furthermore, with estimates that there are some 12 to 13 million potential diabetes sufferers, it has been called a national disease.

In addition, one in four newborn babies suffers from atopic dermatitis.

So why has all this come about? It is because modern medicine aims at treating symptoms; it is allopathic. If you have a fever, you take something to bring it down. If you have a headache, you immediately take a painkiller. No effort is made to sort out *why* the patient has a fever or *why* he or she has a headache. With this kind of symptomatic treatment, it is difficult to effect a basic cure, and the real cause of an illness is often obscured. If we carry on as we are, the number of victims of each illness will continue to increase at a frightening pace.

So does the future look dark? I do not believe so. If we look closely, for example, we can see that the number of tuberculosis (TB) sufferers has decreased dramatically (although, it is true that there have been recent reports of their number increasing). As you know, at one time, TB was called the destroyer of countries and was held in the greatest fear. This was because, once infected, you were almost certain to die, and the disease was known to be extremely infectious. However, even TB lost its terror with the discovery of penicillin and streptomycin. These two drugs, both antibiotics, are not what we would term symptomatic treatment. This is because they attack and kill the root cause of the disease, the tubercle bacillus itself. This is root-cause-oriented treatment itself. Whenever this kind of treatment is discovered, patient numbers show a true and marked decline.

How long it will be before we are able to offer such treatment to the sufferers of the diseases that continue to grow today nobody knows. However, I believe that, in the near future, their numbers will certainly diminish.

# CHAPTER ONE

## WHAT IS PI-WATER?

## THE ROOT CAUSE OF ILLNESS LIES IN THE LOSS OF BIO-ENERGY

Before I explain what Pi-Water is, I would like to mention a little about religion. In the Bible, there are numerous examples of Jesus Christ performing the miracle of healing merely by the laying on of hands. In fact, a large part of the New Testament consists of such examples.

In considering such miracles from the scientific point of view, I believe it is possible that Christ was able to heal sickness by transferring his own bio-energy to the sick. I think it is quite natural that all kinds of sicknesses should be cured by the strong transference of bio-energy. If we consider what sickness really is in the first place, then I believe the root cause of sickness to be the loss of bio-energy.

There are probably those who would say, "No way! AIDS is caused by a virus and TB by the tubercle bacillus." And I would agree with them.

However, I would like them to consider this carefully. Some people sharing a room with somebody who has a cold will catch the cold and some will not. What is the difference between the two? It is probably that one has plenty of bio-energy and the other does not.

The person who has plenty of bio-energy (in certain circumstances, it could probably be termed *immunity*) will not be vulnerable in the presence of the cold virus. I think that it is merely a case of the person with low bio-energy picking up the virus and developing a cold.

Therefore, it is only to be expected that if someone is given a strong booster of bio-energy, they should be able to recover from various kinds of illness.

## PI-WATER CONTAINS BIO-ENERGY

Hitherto, I have been using the rather vague term *bio-energy*. What exactly is this bio-energy that I have been talking about?

There are various types of energy, for example, light energy, electric energy, atomic energy, and so on. However, the energy that we are discussing here is "aura" energy. Aura energy can

be seen in the golden light that is depicted in the background of Buddhist images. It is the shining halo seen above the head of Christ. The color and shape of this aura will differ depending on the individual. Bio-energy is of the same order.

It has been ascertained that there is an extremely powerful aura emanating from high-energy Pi-Water. Unfortunately, this aura cannot be seen by just anybody. However, highly sensitive people, and not just those who are mediums, can see it.

I personally know of nearly 100 people who have been able to ascertain the aura emitted from Pi-Water. Some say that they have seen it rise some 30 to 40 centimeters like a candle flame from the mouth of a container. Others say it was about 10 centimeters. Some people can see the aura and some cannot, although there are those who can feel it with their hand. When such people try to pick up a vessel containing high-energy Pi-Water, they cry out in surprise and let go. They say it "felt just like an electric shock." Therefore, when you try to film this aura energy in a Kirlian photograph, reputed to be able to capture such things, you get a picture of a strong light emanating from such water or from Pi-ceramics.

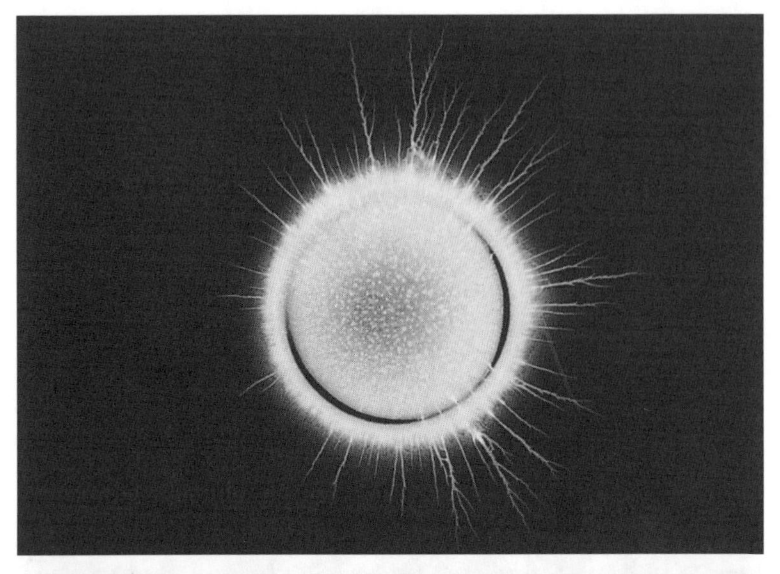

Top: Kirlian photograph of aura from Pi-water
Bottom: Kirlian photograph of aura of Pi-ceramic

Consequently, the correct definition of Pi-Water would be: Water that contains bio-energy, that has aura energy. This is the true nature of Pi-Water, and there are probably those who would find it miraculous. However, I would like you to really understand it.

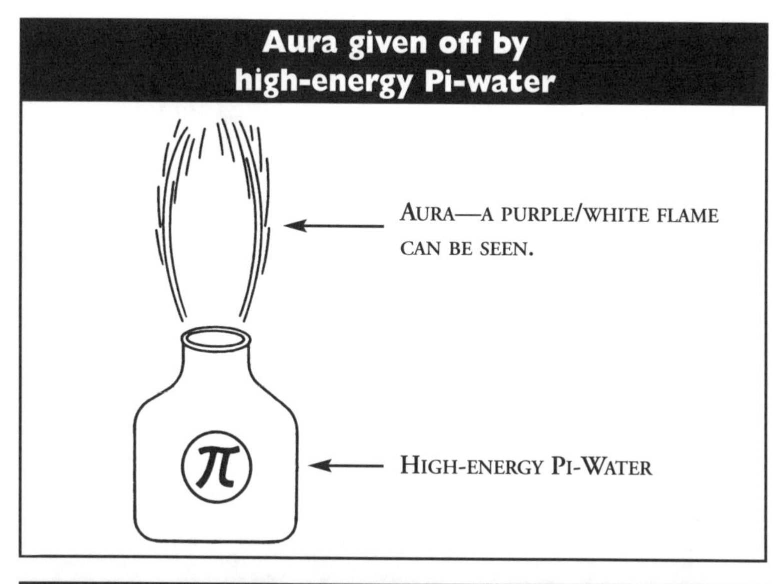


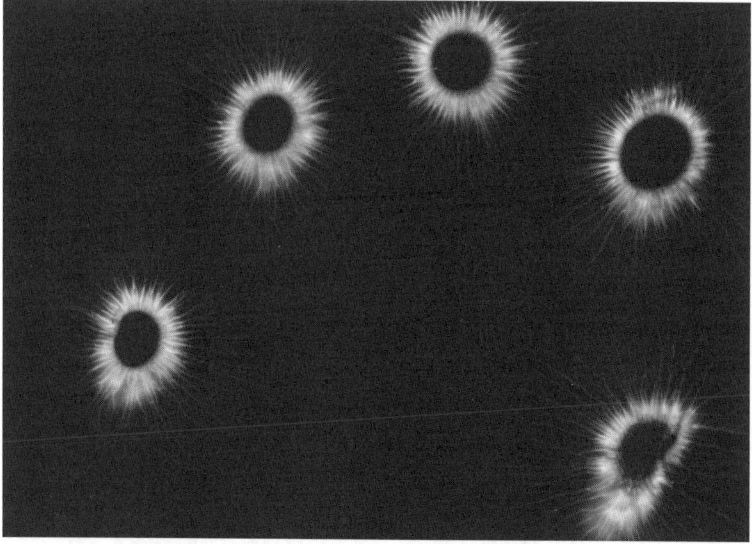

Kirlian photograph of aura emanating from human fingertips

High-energy Pi-Water is known under the generic terms BES and UFO, which are not for sale to the general public, and PAISEIREI. As an example, I have shown the chemical composition of UFO in the table on page 6. There is no fundamental difference between UFO and BES. However, PAISEIREI also contains extract of plants.

| Chemical composition of UFO | |
|---|---|
| Calcium | 22.9 mg/100g; |
| Sodium | 8.14 g/100g; |
| Potassium | 65.8 mg/100g; |
| Magnesium | 856 mg/100g; |
| Iron | micro-quantities |

Taken from data produced by Japan Food Research Laboratories

### How Pi-Water was discovered

As I have described before in my earlier book *The Miracle of Pi-Water*, Pi-Water was discovered through research into the physiology of plant life. The late Professor Yoshiaki Gotoh and Dr. Shoji Yamashita of the Department of Agriculture at Nagoya University had been engaged in research into seedlings. As they tackled the process of differentiation, they realized that an important key to the problem lay in the water content of plants. Later, Dr. Yamashita was to tentatively christen such water, water almost the same as water in a living body, Pi-Water. It then became clear that the particular chemical properties of this kind of Pi-Water were brought about by microscopic quantities of iron ions. Such iron ions exist under conditions of heightened energy. Therefore, they were called ferric ferrous salts.

### The miracle of a fish able to survive in sealed jar

Please look at the photograph on page 7. It shows a goldfish swimming in a hermetically sealed jar. Common sense tells us that such a fish should be dead within 24 hours. This would be only natural as it has no oxygen. However, if it is swimming in Pi-Water, it can survive for two or three months. In one experiment, we achieved a record of six months. In such a situation, we can not just say, "Wow! It's still swimming. Poor thing!" From the standpoint of modern science, no living creature (a goldfish in this case) deprived of oxygen and food should be able to go on living.

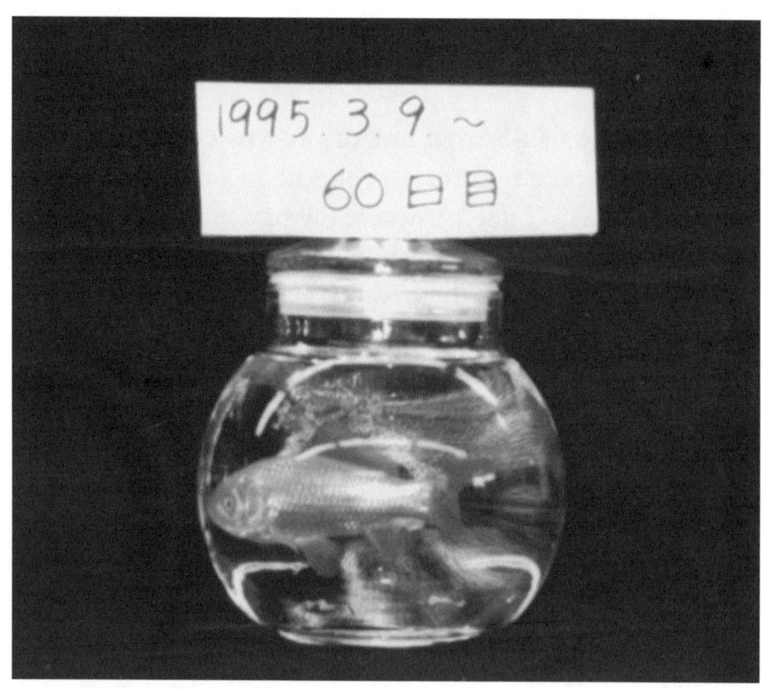


Living goldfish in hermetically sealed jar

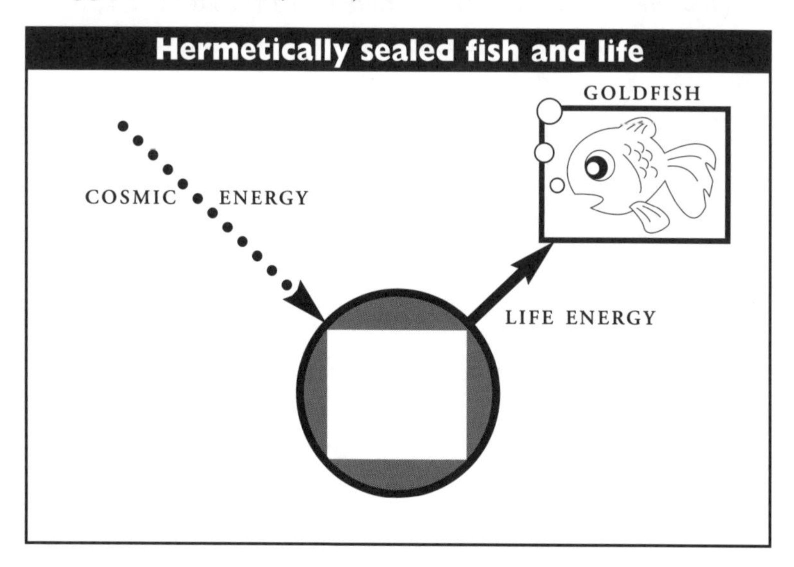

This goldfish forces us to consider important questions as to the nature of breathing and life itself. However, even if we say it's impossible for the fish to survive under these conditions, we still have to consider it as an established fact. So, on consideration, how can we give a satisfactory explanation for this phenomenon?

## THE SOURCE OF PI-WATER ENERGY LIES IN COSMIC ENERGY

Let's now suppose that there is one all-encompassing cosmic energy, although it doesn't necessarily have to be so. It is generally believed that we are surrounded by vast amounts of cosmic energy but that we don't realize it and that other creatures cannot use it.

The reason that animals cannot use this energy is that their own energy waves clash with those of cosmic energy. In order to make use of these cosmic energy waves, it is necessary to tune into them first. It is like tuning into the frequency of radio waves when listening to the radio. It is thought that cosmic energy waves are extremely subtle. Bioenergy waves, being those of a living creature, are rather fuzzy. Therefore, it is difficult for them to tune in with cosmic energy waves.

However, I believe that it is here that Pi-Water helps, probably by acting as an intermediary: it absorbs cosmic energy and emits it as bio-energy. In other words, it acts as a transformer for these waves. If this is the case, then the goldfish should be able to absorb bio-energy as infinitum, as cosmic energy is limitless.

We have seen the case of a goldfish being able to make use of cosmic energy. However, are there examples of a human being able to do the same?

## HOW THE ASCETIC MONKS OF MOUNT HIEI USE COSMIC ENERGY

The monks of Mt.Hiei are known for their extreme ascetic practices. Among these, the most severe is that called "The Trial of the Thousand Days and Summits," where they are expected to run upward of 30 kilometers a day through the mountains continuously for a period of seven years. As it is a thousand days, they should be able to complete it in a little less than three years. So, why does it take seven? Well, this is because various other ascetic trials are also included in the program. For example, they sometimes have to submit to standing under waterfalls or descend to the foot of the mountains, a journey that can be more than 40 kilometers.

What kind of food do monks undergoing such rigorous ascetic training eat? As you might expect, they eat only the very minimum and simplest of foods. It is here that we run into an unexpected question. The monks could be expected to use several thousand calories per day. However, no matter how you calculate it, the amount of calories they can get from such simple and small rations comes to no more than several hundred per day. In other words, the amount of calories they use far exceeds the number of calories they take in.

The difference is so great that modern nutritional science cannot account for it. The phenomenon of these monks of Mount Hiei has been called a "miracle of nutrition." In other words, it is impossible to explain. What is happening on Mount Hiei is well known to nutritional scientists.

So how can such an incredible thing be possible? I believe that there is a flaw in the thinking of nutritional science. When you really think about it, nutritional science is no more than the science of combustion. It puts human beings into the same category as the motor car, something that runs simply by burning gasoline. The major precept of nutritional science is that energy can only be absorbed into the human body as food via the mouth. But is this really so?

If we accept that there is another possible source of energy other than food, then it becomes easy to understand.

What if we once more assume the existence of cosmic energy? Earlier I said that living organisms could not utilize cosmic energy. However, it is here that human and other living creatures differ. By long ascetic training, humans can approach a state of enlightenment. Could it not be that, in this state, one's own vibrations are able to spread out into space and unite with cosmic energy waves?

The "Trial of the Thousand Days and Summits" is a tough challenge of seven years' duration. Not everybody could be expected to undertake such a rigorous ordeal. Ordinary human beings like us would probably end up giving up within one week. All those monks who are to undertake the seven years are first set a five-year ordeal. Only those monks who show promise, coming close to a state of enlightenment during this first test, may attempt the trial of a thousand days. It could be said that the program of ascetic training at Mount Hiei is extremely logical in its design.

If you are wondering whether the monks who have completed this thousand day trial die young by overstraining themselves, the answer is no, not at all. All of them lead long and healthy lives afterward. From this, it should be clear to all of us that we eat far too much.

I have given an example from Japan, but I have also heard of such an example from India. There, great ascetics claiming to have reached one with the Buddha while still in the flesh, who have reached a state of enlightenment, undergo a remarkable trial: they are buried in wooden caskets to a depth of some four meters for a period of six months. They are then dug out and are able to be revived in perfect health.

Unless we look at this Indian phenomenon in the same way as the hermetically sealed goldfish, then it is impossible to explain. That is to say, it is easier to explain a number of phenomena in the human world if we assume the existence of cosmic energy.

### VANITY IS ENERGY

After describing the Mount Hiei phenomenon, I would like to talk a little about Buddhism. When we speak of religion, the image is usually one of something unscientific. But is this really the case? I have already quoted from the Bible earlier. If we explain the Bible in that way, you will see that the events described in that book could be seen as surprisingly scientific. I am convinced that the things written there are by no means unfounded. However, the Bible is western in conception.

So what is the eastern concept? Naturally, if we are to talk of the eastern concept, it has to be Buddhism. Among Buddhist teachings, the most important is that of the Hannyashinkyo. This book consists of only 276 calligraphic characters and is the shortest such religious book in the world. However, these 276 characters have somehow been passed down to us through many millennia. It is much older than the Bible and is historically incomparable.

Among these 276 characters, eight stand out as being of central importance. They stand for "the vanity of all things" and "this vanity makes up all the things of the phenomenal world." In general, the character that represents "things" is explained as symbolizing "the material world," "the phenomenal world," or "this world."

However, the explanation for the character representing "vanity" is difficult. It is said that to understand this word is to understand the Hannyashinkyo. Usually, vanity is explained as emptiness, the void. Therefore, we would enter the world described in the *Heike Monogatari*, a world where everything is in a state of flux and nothing is permanent. But is this really the case? I would argue that it is probably not.

Could not *emptiness* be *energy*? It cannot be seen with the naked eye; it cannot be felt by touch: the very concept of *energy* did not exist a few thousand years ago. Could it not be that the only way they could express this concept was through the word *emptiness*? Of course, I speak here only of the scientific aspect of the Hannyashinkyo.

If we take vanity to mean energy, then we find ourselves changing the word *things* to mean "phenomena." Consequently, we have the concept of *material* meaning "energy," and *energy* meaning "material."

## EINSTEIN SCIENTIFICALLY CORROBORATES THE HANNYASHINKYO

Albert Einstein's special theory of relativity is well known. It can be formulated simply as $e=mc^2$. *E* gives us energy, *m* gives us mass, and *c* gives us the speed of light. This means that energy is equal to the square of mass multiplied by the speed of light. Put another way, it is saying that energy is mass, and mass is energy.

In other words, here Albert Einstein offers us scientific proof of what the Hannyashinkyo is saying. I think that it is amazing that this has gone unnoticed. When you think of it that way, it really points out the fact that, while the Hannyashinkyo is, of course, a religious work, it is also a philosophical treatise and a remarkable scientific work at the same time.

Far from religion and science being two completely unrelated things, they can be seen as pursuing the same goal through a different methodology.

Human beings can absorb cosmic energy and convert it into bio-energy once they have attained certain psychological and physical states. However, up until now, only a special chosen few have been able to do this. The chemistry of Pi is an energy conversion system, which allows ordinary people to do the same. I believe that Pi-Water is the substance that holds the key to this.

## HOW DOES PI-WATER HELP PEOPLE RECOVER FROM ILLNESS?

Pi-Water has long been shown to be especially effective against an extremely wide range of illnesses. However, why that should be so is not known. Despite this fact, its effectiveness has been so conspicuous that the circle of medical doctors using it has continued to grow. The results are reported to be very good.

In this, the age of science, providing a logical explanation for the mechanism of Pi-Water (that is, a scientific explanation of how it actually works) is necessry to persuade people of its efficacy. From this standpoint, the Association for Research and Propagation of Bio Energy System (President: Dr. Noboru Ijima, Emeritus Professor, School of Medicine, St Marianna University) was founded in order to conduct extensive research into Pi-Water and to make the results known worldwide.

From the research conducted by this group, one epoch-making piece of evidence has emerged regarding the mystery of Pi-Water. To illustrate this, I would like to discuss the remarkable antagonistic action of Pi-Water against calcium.

What is the function of calcium in the human body? Probably the first thing that comes to mind is its role in forming bones and teeth. Certainly, the largest deposits of calcium in the body are located in the bones and teeth. However, apart from that, calcium plays an extremely important role in fulfilling the physiological functions of the human body.

For example, it disperses into microscopic quantities in the blood and serves as a coagulant. If our bodies did not have any calcium, our blood would not coagulate. The amount of calcium in our bloodstream accounts for only one ten-thousandth of our total calcium. However, that supermicroscopic amount of calcium, that one ten-thousandth, is to be found inside the cellular matrix.

The amount of calcium in a cell is only one-hundred-millionth of that found in bones and teeth. It could be said to be almost nonexistent. It is this supermicroscopic amount of calcium that supports the activity of that cell. If it weren't there, there would be a breakdown in the cell's important internal information transmission system. However, if too much calcium is present, it can cause great problems.

For example, it is known that there is a high concentration of calcium in cancerous cells. Cancer is also known as *carcinoma*, referring to the uncontrolled calcium in the cells. It could be said that this word symbolizes the extreme undesirability of too much calcium in cells.

Too much calcium in the cells not only causes cancer but also puts stress on the cells, eventually causing them to die. It has been found that Pi-Water acts as an antagonist to prevent cells from absorbing too much calcium, thus keeping it at normal levels. Moreover, it has already been ascertained that Pi-Water also functions to eliminate activated oxygen and heighten the body's immune system.

These are but a few functions of Pi-Water. However, it could probably be said that this helps explain how Pi-Water acts to help people recover from a number of adult, that is to say, lifestyle-related, diseases. I feel it would be no mistake to think of the action of Pi-Water as being somehow intimately tied in with the immune system with which each of us is endowed.

### ENERGY WATER AND HIGH-ENERGY PI-WATER

I sometimes receive inquiries about the difference between the water you can get by using the Pi-Water Purifier and high-energy Pi-Water itself. They both have water with auric energy (bio-energy) in common. In that meaning, they both provide Pi-Water. However, the level of energy is where they differ. At this point in time, it is not possible to accurately measure the exact amount of energy produced. But, I believe the disparity to be somewhere in the region of three digits.

The Pi-Water Purifier was originally developed to enable healthy people to enjoy tasty tea and coffee; its aim was to support their current level of health. On the other hand, high-energy Pi-Water was developed to help people who were concerned about their level of health. This is a point I would like to make clear.

However, even though the level of energy in high-energy Pi-Water is extremely high, it doesn't mean that the Pi-Water Purifier is no longer necessary. On the contrary, it could probably be said that the Pi-Water Purifier is an indispensable part of every household. Why? Because:

- It is an essential condition for healthy living that each and every member of a household drinks as much good, high-energy water as possible. There is a lot of truth in the old saying that "water is the foundation of health." I totally agree. It is a mistake to rely on medicines to safeguard your health.

- In order to dilute high-energy Pi-Water, it is essential to use the Pi-Water Purifier. High-energy Pi-Water diluted with tap water or other negative energy water will reduce effectiveness by more than half.
- If we were to heighten the energy level of the water produced by the Pi-Water Purifier (a technical impossibility, anyway), would it be the same as high-energy Pi-Water? No, it would not.

As I will describe later in this chapter in the section entitled "Eastern Medicine and Improvement in Health," the consumption of high-energy Pi-Water sometimes brings about an improvement reaction (what is known in eastern medicine as the Mengen reaction). The unsuspecting consumer sometimes mistakes this reaction for a side effect, which can lead to a big misunderstanding.

One often hears stories of various problems such as atopic dermatitis, hay fever, and period pains being cured by the water produced by the Pi-Water Purifier. The level of energy currently available from the Pi-Water Purifier is enough. I believe it to be the optimum amount.

### How to take high-energy Pi-Water

As I have already mentioned earlier, high-energy Pi-Water is, by way of a development code or product name, generically termed a BES or UFO or is known as PAISEIREI. In many treatments that we have seen so far, Pi-Water has proved effective against a number of complaints. However, unfortunately, a detailed procedure for taking it is not available. Therefore, I have given below what may be considered a general guide to its use:

1. Dissolve the appropriate amount of high-energy Pi-Water in one full cup of water (approximately 150 ml) and mix

well. Drink on rising, before lunch, and at bedtime, three times a day.

2. The appropriate amount of Pi-Water is given as follows:
   1st week: 3 drops, 3 times per day (total of 9 drops per day)
   2nd week: 5 drops, 3 times per day (total of 15 drops per day)
   3rd week: 10 drops, 3 times per day (total of 30 drops per day)
   4th week: 20 drops, 3 times per day (total of 60 drops per day)
3. The following gives a general guide to the correct dosage:
   a. Cancer—30 drops, 3 times per day (total of 90 drops per day)
   b. Diabetes, hepatitis, stomach ulcers, heart disease, asthma, high blood pressure, etc.—20 drops, 3 times per day (total of 60 drops per day)
   c. Renal failure, rheumatism, atopic dermatitis, hay fever, etc.—10 drops, 3 times per day (total of 30 drops)
   d. Menstrual pains, constipation, bad hangovers, other minor disorders—10 drops, 1 time per day (total of 10 drops per day)
   e. Maintenance of health—3 drops, 3 times per day (total of 9 drops per day)

The above is only an approximate standard, and the dose will vary according to the symptoms of each individual.

Using the above recommendtions, when the patient becomes aware that the condition is starting to improve, he or she should continue to take the same dosage. An improvement should normally be evident within one week of beginning treatment.

4. Note:
   a. On dilution, it is better to use water from the Pi-Water Purifier, but if that is not available, then use mineral water at the very least. Tap water or tea is not suitable. It will cut the effect by more than half. (Tap water is oxidized water. Pi-Water is deoxidized water and therefore will conflict with it. Tea contains tannic acid, and Pi-Water contains iron ions. The two together will produce black deposits.)

b. Please be sure to follow your physician's instructions at all times. It is not possible to be cured just by Pi-Water alone without following such medical advice.
c. Generally speaking, taking Pi-Water at the same time as standard, synthetic medicines is not recommended. However, until the condition stabilizes, continue to take both (two to three months). After the condition has stabilized, gradually reduce the dosage of medicine. Pi-Water has the ability to revitalize the body's immune system, decrease excess calcium deposits, disperse activated oxygen, and so on. But, it is undesirable to consume Pi-Water alongside synthetic medicines that have the ability to conflict with it for any length of time. Doing so will negate the effect of the Pi-Water.
d. As an improvement reaction, when the body constitution starts to change, a number of minor problems may occur such as the following: (1) you will feel physically lighter; (2) urination will become more frequent because of the body's metabolism being stimulated; (3) a slight fever; (4) fatigue; (5) there may be an increase in gas because of the stomach's being stimulated; (6) the stool may become soft, although this may be overcome by decreasing the overall water intake; (7) constipation caused by water in the colon being re-assimilated, although this may be remedied by increasing the overall water intake; ( 8) rash. However, all of this only shows that the treatment is actually working. If you are worried, you may decrease the dosage by one half or stop taking it temporarily. In so doing, the symptoms should disappear within three to four days. It is important to understand that this reaction is most likely to manifest itself at the body's weakest points or those places that have some history of problems.
e. Drink good, high-energy water as much as possible each day (two to three liters per day).
f. Avoid psychological stress at all costs. It is important to be mentally calm. (It is said that unusual stress can lead

to cancer, stomach ulcers, atopic dermatitis, and so on.)

g. The first changes should occur within one month of beginning treatment. (you will start to feel physically lighter, and so on).

h. It is extremely rare, but with very sensitive people, a dosage of three drops three times per day (total of nine drops per day) can sometimes cause a violent improvement reaction. In such a case, suspend intake for a time. After symptoms have disappeared, begin again at the dosage program given below, gradually increasing as recommended:

   1st week: 1 drop, 1 time per day (total of 1 drop per day)
   2nd week: 1 drop, 3 times per day (total of 3 drops per day)
   3rd week: 2 drops, 3 times per day (total of 6 drops per day)

   After this, please return to the dosage regime described earlier.

## EASTERN MEDICINE AND THE IMPROVEMENT REACTION

The history of medicine can be broadly divided into two strands: that of eastern, and that of western medicine. In Japan, since the Meiji restoration, eastern medicine has been denigrated, and an all-out effort has been made to unify everything under western medicine. However, I believe that eastern medicine is now being re-evaluated. In neighboring China and Korea, we already even have universities specializing in eastern medicine.

There is a tendency among people to illogically wish for a kind of shortcut: to want a synthesis of the best that both eastern and western medicine has to offer. However, this is not as easy as it might sound. Not only is the thinking different between the two but also the very way illnesses are defined.

How different are their approaches? In general terms, eastern medicine attempts to draw out symptoms, whereas western medicine attempts to suppress them.

Let's look at a couple of examples. One older man in his fifties had a skin eruption as a child. His mother put ointment on it to draw out the rash, and it was cured. This kind of medicine to draw out a rash is an eastern medicine concept. By putting on such ointment, the pus is drawn out, and a cure is easily effected.

Western medicine doesn't have this kind of concept. Using surgery, the affected part is removed, or large amounts of antagonistic (allopathic) drugs are prescribed. This is part of the "suppress the symptoms" mentality. Again, with eastern medicine, when someone catches a cold or develops a temperature, he or she is required to rest in a warm room, to cover up with a blanket, and to sweat it out. As the sweat pours out of the body, the cold or temperature miraculously disappears. Western medicine would immediately prescribe something to take the temperature down. Western medicine is easy to understand, but it tends to rely overmuch on external remedies.

On taking high-energy Pi-Water, an improvement reaction will sometimes occur. In the case of atopic dermatitis, this reaction is often rather violent. However, if the patient continues to take the high-energy Pi-Water, the symptoms will be drawn out, and a cure will be easily effected.

Pi-Water is especially effective against hepatitis. However, when sufferers first take large amounts of high-energy Pi-Water, they are liable to become fatigued (this is also true of people with weak livers). If they continue to take it, this fatigue will disappear, and the hepatitis will be cured. However, if they take a liver function test when they have this fatigue, their liver function tests, that is, GOT and GPT levels, will show an increase.

Looked at from the eastern medicine point of view, these effects that occur in atopic dermatitis and hepatitis are easily understood. But from the western medicine viewpoint, they are mistaken for side effects.

Of course, violent reactions of any kind are to be viewed as undesirable. If they occur, you should immediately reduce dosage by half or temporarily suspend intake.

Now, we will go on to look at what kind of effect Pi-Water has had on various adult complaints such as cancer. I would then like to explain as simply as possible the true nature of Pi-Water and how it can be used in our daily lives.

# CHAPTER TWO

❁ ❁ ❁

# LIFE ENHANCING PI-WATER

## How does Pi-Water make cancer disappear?

First, in order to help you realize the effectiveness of Pi-Water in helping cure illnesses, I would like to give a few typical examples.

One case concerned a man with a cancer in his left ear that then spread into his brain. At this point, surgery was out of the question so the physicians tried radiotherapy and chemotherapy, but there was no improvement. By the standards of modern medicine, the situation was hopeless.

Then, the doctor in charge, with the patient's consent, tried high-energy Pi-Water (BES). Treatment began on the 12th of March, and by the 22nd of April the tumor in the patient's ear had shrunk to a size of six centimeters. However, almost no change could be seen in the cancer-infected area of the brain. They therefore decided to try increasing the dosage, and within one week an improvement could be seen. Two months later, both the tumor in the ear and the tumor in the brain had completely disappeared.

Let me give you another example. A man in his 70s was informed that he was suffering from stomach cancer. It was still early-stage, but it was already too late to excise it with an endoscope, so the doctor recommended surgery. However, the patient refused, saying that he was already old and that he didn't want to undergo surgery.

However, realizing that he just couldn't leave things to go on as they were, the patient sought advice at a clinic specializing in treatment based on dietary and traditional Chinese cures. The head of the hospital said, "We have this." What they had was Pi-Water.

On inquiry, it seems that many patients had had good results with it. So, in conjunction with a dietary regime, the patient decided to give it a try. Two months later, he went back for a checkup to the hospital that had been urging him to have surgery. Miraculously, the cancer had completely disappeared.

In cases like this, where the cancer is still in its early-stage, it sometimes naturally goes into remission or disappears. And I think there is no doubt that the strict dietary regime he had been following played some part. However, I also believe that the effect of the Pi-Water was also very important. The following case will explain why I believe this to be so.

In this instance the patient was man in his 60s. On receiving a checkup as part of a group of people, he was informed that he needed to have another one, this time as a private patient. He was informed that he had a large, two centimeter tumor at the pylorus of his stomach. The tumor itself wasn't so large, but it had taken root to a depth of some four to five centimeters, so he was told that he must have it surgically removed.

He, too, did not want to undergo surgery. But, being a mere layman, he felt he couldn't really refuse the advice of a doctor. Reluctantly, he arranged an appointment to have surgery two months later and returned home. On telling his brother what had happened, his brother said, "I know a really good doctor. Why don't you give him a try?" So he went to the same clinic I mentioned earlier, a clinic where Pi-Water is well regarded in such treatment. He then proceeded to drink Pi-Water without fail until the day of the surgery.

Two months passed, and time for the pre-operative checkup finally came around. Getting up at five in the morning, he went all the way to the hospital for a thorough examination. Afterward, the doctor looked puzzled and said, "That's strange. There's absolutely nothing resembling a tumor anywhere!"

Again, the cancer had disappeared. In this case, the patient had not, however, been on any kind of dietary regime. Even so, an even more advanced cancer than described before had vanished. With this kind of evidence, it is difficult to deny the effectiveness of Pi-Water. Such examples of Pi-Water's helping cure illnesses are too numerous to recount.

## PI-WATER HAS THE POWER TO MAXIMIZE NATURAL HEALING POWER

As I mentioned before in Chapter One, all these examples involve the use of Pi-Water by practicing physicians and real patients. And in particular, the extreme effectiveness of Pi-Water in combating end-stage cancer has been regarded with astonishment in clinics everywhere.

Dr. Noboru Ijima, Emeritus Professor of the School of Medicine, St Marianna University, has been very interested in Pi-Water and has had the following to say about its astonishing powers: "We, each of us, have the ability within our own bodies to fight cancer. It could be said, for example, to resemble using the brakes to park a car on a steep slope. In the same way, the power of the brakes can also be used to stop a car climbing a hill. It seems that Pi-Water has the power to enhance the equivalent power in human beings."

Pi-Water has quite a long history and has been useful in the cure of a number of illnesses to date. However, many of the instances of its powers rest on personal testimony, and, therefore, there have been some problems with its being recognized by the medical profession.

However, on the other hand, recently it has been drawing attention among medical professionals themselves. For example, on the 30th of March 1997, the Third Pi-Water Symposium was held at a place called Big Site in Tokyo (sponsored by the Association for Research and Propagation for Bio Energy System). It drew a great deal of attention, and a number of interesting things were said, as I shall go on to describe:

- **Pi-Water is viable for all types of patient.**
  "I believe I may have used high-energy Pi-Water (BES) in more patients than anyone else in Japan. It really does work. Of course, this may not entirely be due just to the use of BES. But, as a supplement in treatment, I believe it to be an extremely powerful weapon. At the moment, I am treating some 100 terminal cancer patients. Even those showing widespread metastasis are showing good signs of improvement. Further, it has also been very effective in patients suffering from the itchiness caused by atopic dermatitis and still others with cataracts. It has been three years since the

book *High-energy Pi-Water Overcomes Cancer*, containing the collected clinical results of treatment with Pi-Water, was published by Kosaido. Since [the treatment results]were announced, Pi-Water has proved clinically effective in an incomparably large number of instances."(Dr. Takashi Tsurumi, the president of Tsurumi Medical Clinic)

- **Some doctors are convinced of the effectiveness of Pi-Water in enhancing the immune system.**
  "I always test Pi-Water patients' cellular matrix using a dark-field microscope. I have also used 20 volunteers and had them drink only Pi-Water. One particular patient showed an unchanging white blood cell count. I had him drink 30 drops of high-energy Pi-Water and then checked again five minutes later. This time, the white blood cells had begun to change, and I was able to verify that his blood pH value had returned to normal. I believe that high-energy Pi-Water has the ability to enhance the immune system." (Doctor of Natural Medicine, Dr Alfonso Won, Canada)
- **There is confirmation that it is extremely effective in cases of MRSA.**
  "It is common for long-stay patients to develop bedsores, and these are very difficult to cure. It is known that the biggest reason for this difficulty is MRSA infection. On discussing this problem with Dr. Makino, I tried high-energy Pi-Water (UFO). I first used a solution of 1 to 50 parts but found it to have no effect. However, on using an undiluted solution, the patient began to show signs of recovery." (Head of Towa Hospital, Dr. Tsunamasa Inou)

The above represents only a small sample. But I believe this will help you understand how Pi-Water is being used at various hospitals and clinics.

In a clinical research project carried out by another group examining the clinical effectiveness of Pi-Water, it was found to be effective in 91.1 percent of cases (103 out of 113 cases).

These were all types of illnesses that modern medicine has problems treating, such as cancer, hepatitis, diabetes, and so on. I believe it could be said that it would now be difficult to dispute the usefulness of Pi-Water in combating sickness and improving health.

## CLEAR CONNECTION BETWEEN ILLNESS AND ACTIVATED OXYGEN

We are all physical beings. However, we live by using the energy that we all create inside our bodies. Everything, the way our blood circulates, the movement of our hands and feet, the act of thinking, all of these things depend on such energy.

So, how is this energy created? Inside our cells there is something called mitochondria. This is thought to be the place where such energy is created, a kind of power station. When we breathe in oxygen, it is carried to the mitochondria. Nutrients, too, are absorbed in the same way.

These nutrients are then burned up by oxygen creating something called ATP. This is what constitutes energy in the human body. The problem is that, regardless of amount, when we create such energy, we also produce a harmful substance known as activated oxygen. This activated oxygen is a highly reactive oxygen molecule, which when steadily produced in large amounts in the body can lead to various problems.

The cells' genes, for example, will be attacked. Furthermore, when activated oxygen binds with unsaturated fatty acids, it creates the corrosive element, lipofuscin (a pigment found in the aging process). If large amounts of this build up in the body, various kinds of damage can be caused.

In order to create energy we have to absorb oxygen from the atmosphere. However, this oxygen then creates harmful activated oxygen. Of course, not all activated oxygen is harmful. This is because it is used to attack various kinds of harmful bacteria in the human body. If it only destroyed harmful substances, all would be well. Unfortunately, this is not the case. According to recent research, activated oxygen damages a certain type of gene causing ordinary cells to become cancerous. The truth is, activated oxygen can trigger cancer.

Why should the oxygen so necessary to all of us also be so harmful? There are experimental data that give us the answer to this question. For example, an animal kept in an atmosphere of 100 percent oxygen will die within approximately one week. Also, in humans an increase in exercise can increase oxygen intake and thus accelerate the aging process. These facts have been ascertained by detailed research. In other words, greater oxygen intake leads to a shorter life span.

Why is it that professional athletes, people who have trained their bodies far more than ordinary people, don't necessarily live long? This is because in exercising they increase their consumption of oxygen.

When the amount of exercise is increased, a corresponding amount of oxygen is required. As the rate at which the mitochondria work increases, so too does the opportunity to produce harmful activated oxygen. Conversely, animals that don't expend much energy in exercise live longer. It is a well-known fact that, in comparison to animals that don't, animals that hibernate exhibit a much slower aging process and live longer.

In the case of humans, too, there has long been the saying, "Always leave a little room when you eat." Not overtaxing the mitochondria works on the same principle. When we eat large amounts of food, we can produce large quantities of fuel in the form of ATP. However, at the same time, we will also produce a corresponding amount of activated oxygen that will exert a negative influence on the body.

In other words, too much activated oxygen is harmful, yet too little can cause problems, too. One problem caused by not enough activated oxygen is that of chronic hardening of lumps of flesh. Spongy tumors appear on the surface of the skin and are difficult to eradicate. On close investigation, it would appear that this is due to old cells not dying off because of a deficiency in activated oxygen.

This is a negative effect caused by a lack of activated oxygen. However, if, on the other hand, we look at the situation where there is a surfeit of activated oxygen, then we find infantile retinopathy. Thus, both a lack and a surfeit of activated oxygen are to be regarded as negative.

Recently, the connection between activated oxygen and illness has become very clear. It would appear that in most adult illnesses there will be a surfeit or a deficit of activated oxygen, and, depending on the degree, the severity of the illness will increase or decrease accordingly. Therefore, if one had to give a fundamental reason for much illness, then one would have no choice but to name activated oxygen.

Now, one of the effects of Pi-Water is to remove activated oxygen. The reason why Pi-Water is so effective against such a wide range of illnesses is because it possesses this property.

For example, Pi-Water relieves skin complaints. It is good for diabetes. It is effective in fighting cancer and preventing aging. The general wisdom that maintains that anything that is effective for a number of different illnesses can't be much good does not apply to Pi-Water. The fact is that Pi-Water has the power to combat the harm caused by the common root cause of a number of problems. That is to say, activated oxygen.

## AGING, CANCER, HEART DISEASE, AND DIABETES SHARE A COMMON ROOT

Why do people age? This has long been a mystery to mankind. Aging and death are a path that we all will have to tread. Many opinions have been offered as to why that should be.

For example, aging and death are determined by genetics; toxins build up in the intestines and the body poisons itself; and so on. There are many theories. Currently, the theory that is attracting the most attention is that of activated oxygen (free radical theory). Just how is activated oxygen connected to the aging process?

In the nucleus of cells, at the ends of the chromosomes, can be found something called *telomeres*. During aging, these ends are cut off, steadily becoming shorter and shorter. This phenomenon of aging has recently become clear through advances made in the science of genetic engineering.

Activated oxygen works to promote this shortening of the telomere, which, in turn, counteracts cell division. This decrease in cell division gives us what is otherwise known as the aging phenomenon. And what promotes all this is activated oxygen.

Again, with cancer, there are certain genes that act to stem the growth of cancerous genes and cells. However, activated oxygen acts to promote cancer by activating cancerous genes. As a result, the cancer is accelerated.

There is a phenomenon in cells known as *apoptosis*. This refers to the "suicide" of cells, that is, the self-destruction of unwanted cells and foreign substances. In contrast, we also have something known as *necrosis*. This refers to the death of cells, but rather as "homicide." At the cellular level, these are the two ways in which a cell will die.

Recently, apoptosis has been drawing a lot of attention. In cancer, when activated oxygen destroys those genes that promote cellular apoptosis, the cancer gains in strength.

Pi-Water is able to combat this negative effect of activated oxygen. The ability of Pi-Water to function to activate cells and suppress cancer has been clinically confirmed. I hope the above explanation will help you to understand how this works.

In this, the aging society, one problem that is attracting a lot of attention at the moment is that of dementia. There is one kind of dementia resulting from damage to the blood vessels of the brain and Alzheimer's, whose cause is unclear. It is said that this kind of dementia, too, is caused by a reduction in the nerve fibers through modification of the nerve cells by activated oxygen.

It is also impossible to deny the role of activated oxygen in senile dementia resulting from a rapid decline in cells. Again, recent reports showing that amyloid B protein produced in the brain of persons with Alzheimer's increases activated oxygen that then attacks the nerves in the brain have also attracted attention.

Next, let's look at various problems that may arise through damage to the blood vessels in the brain. What is the role of activated oxygen in problems characterized by blood either collecting or hemorrhaging in the brain, such as brain infarctions, apoplexy, strokes, and so on? Contact with activated oxygen will cause a surplus of lipids to be produced in the cell wall. As I mentioned earlier, this constitutes a physical decay and contributes to a number of problems such as the blocking of blood vessels and the oxidation of blood cholesterol. This will lead to conditions like hardening of the arteries, heart disease, brain disorders, and so on.

It can be seen from what I have mentioned that the three main killers in Japan, aging and cancer, brain disorders, and heart disease, are all connected to the problem of activated oxygen. That is to say, they all share the same root cause.

Next in ranking to these three major killers we have diabetes. Diabetes is a dangerous illness that can act as a trigger for other diseases such as hardening of the arteries, heart disease, and cancer. There is much clinical evidence of Pi-Water's extreme effectiveness in combating this particular disease.

In diabetes, insulin is created from beta cells in the pancreas. Perhaps because the amount is insufficient or because insulin functions inadequately, the blood sugar value (the amount of glucose in the blood) rises rapidly leading to a number of problems. Currently, diabetes is categorized as insulin dependent and non-insulin dependent types. It is said that the most common form in Japan is non-insulin dependent, a type that is thought to be heavily influenced by environmental factors such as stress.

When we look at all this closely, whether the role played by activated oxygen is large or small, it is abundantly clear that it does very much have a role in all of these adult diseases. Moreover, modern medicine is unable to offer any effective remedy to most of these serious adult diseases. That is the very reason why Pi-Water with its ability to combat activated oxygen is so valuable. In this I believe it could be said to be irreplaceable.

### The strength of Pi-Water is its naturalness

I have given a fairly negative connotation to the character of activated oxygen, yet, as I have said before, it is very much a double-edged sword. In the right amount it will serve to protect the body, but if a surplus arises, then it will damage healthy cells. In other words, as I described earlier, it will cause various adult diseases, accelerate aging, and so on.

One can summarize that activated oxygen is always being created in a surplus because modern man has lost all the former naturalness from his lifestyle; he has adopted a way of life that is alien to the natural cycle of things.

Therefore, recently, movement toward the use of antioxidant drugs to block activated oxygen, from the point of view of preventing illness, has been increasing. The main focus has been on acid-fast substances such as Vitamins C and E, beta-carotene, catechin, flavonoid, uric acid, and so on. How effective these are against such conditions as cancer and myocardial infarction is being enthusiastically researched worldwide.

For example, currently more than 1,000 people are taking part in an experiment at Louisiana State university in the United States to ascertain how effective Vitamin C and beta-carotene are. In France, some 3,000 people are involved in attempting to find out how effective Vitamins C and E are as preventatives. At the same time, researchers are looking at their possible role in prevention of stomach cancer.

One might have expected that there is no room left for research into the role of something like vitamins. The fact that they are undertaking such research at all shows that they have probably realized that in the traditional approach to medical, pharmaceutical, and nutritional science something has been left out.

From the traditional point of view, it is unthinkable that such nutrients might have a useful role to play in the treatment of serious diseases. It is generally accepted that they are important as nutrients, but it had been thought that nothing more could be expected of them. However, now the idea that these everyday substances may have some hidden power is gaining currency.

In Australia, looking for a treatment in the fight against skin cancer, some 1,700 people are currently involved in experiments aimed at ascertaining the efficacy of the commonplace nutrient beta-carotene. Again, in one medical school in the United States, some 1,000 people are being given beta-carotene and Vitamins E and C in work on cancer of the colon.

Moreover, in a huge clinical trial currently under way at Washington University, 17,000 smokers are being given beta-carotene in research on lung cancer. According to data obtained from certain reports from the above research, it has proved effective in certain circumstances. However, other data suggest that, however much you may give a patient, it has no correlation with prevention of the disease.

In China massive research programs have been carried out using 30,000 subjects, but no satisfactory results were obtained. At Harvard University, 22,000 subjects were given beta-carotene and aspirin to study their role in preventing myocardial infarctions, but their efficacy was not confirmed.

On the one hand we have "Yes, it's effective" and on the other we have "No, there is no evidence." This is a common picture. The reason for this seems to lie in differences in the quality of nutrient used. In other words, even if we take the same Vitamin C, for example, there will be a difference in effectiveness between that obtained naturally through vegetables and fruit and that ingested as synthetic medicine.

Even if we learn only this fact, then these experiments are significant. It could probably be said that through these experiments human beings are being taught how important it is to "live in harmony with nature." Pi-Water has a different effect from these other nutrients, but, on analysis of its contents, it can be seen as consistent with high quality water containing minerals.

We find that there is a rich variety of famous and effective waters that nature has to offer us. Such water might be called natural Pi-Water. However, as far as I've been able to find out, when comparing such water to Pi-Water, the effect is always weaker. In other words, Pi-Water is far more effective than any other water that nature has to offer us.

### THE SIGNIFICANCE OF PI-WATER'S SMALL CLUSTERS

When discussing the quality of water, the topic of cluster size—whether they are big or small—often comes up. Until recently, when judging the quality of water, the only criteria considered were the constituent components it had or should have. However, we now have the additional question of clusters.

Water is made up of two parts hydrogen and one part oxygen. However, in reality, there is no water containing just two parts hydrogen. At the very minimum, it will contain between five to 12 parts water molecules. This grouping of elements is known as *clustering*.

It is thought that the smaller the cluster, the more healthful the water. Why? Because the smaller the cluster, the more permeable the water and the more it will be absorbed thoroughly into the body. However, at the moment there is no method for directly measuring clusters. Therefore, we usually have to use an NMR (nuclear magnetic resonance) device and measure clusters indirectly ( in units of hertz).

When I tested my local water at Hazu-cho in Aichi prefecture, I found it to contain 128 hertz. The smaller the value, the smaller the clusters. On putting this same water through the Pi-Water Purifier, I was able to obtain a reading of only 53 hertz.

Even if I cite such examples one after the other, it would be difficult to grasp their significance. As far as I know, of all the records I have examined, I have found no record of any value approaching this. A reading of 60 hertz would be regarded as the very highest quality of water. Therefore, I believe Pi-Water to be among the very highest quality water in the world, that is, water with the lowest cluster values.

Why do the clusters reduce so radically when water is passed through the Pi-Water Purifier? Because the Purifier contains special ceramics that turn water into Pi-Water, which in turn gives off auric energy. It is hypothesized that this energy then serves to break down these clusters of water molecules.

In other words, clusters of 30, 40, or 50 are broken down by the auric energy into smaller clusters of 10, 8, or 6. Because of this, the power of the water is vastly increased. It has long been said that water has medicinal properties and that water alone could help prevent adult diseases, slow the aging process, and promote beautiful skin.

It had been thought that this was largely due to its stimulating the body's metabolism, but now it is said to be more complicated and have an even more subtle effect. The latent power of water is so very great that it has even been suggested that if water with clusters of only five molecules were possible, then we would no longer have any need for medicine. I believe that Pi-Water can offer us clusters somewhere in the that order of size. If that were not so, it is unthinkable that, as just water, it could be so effective in combating so many different diseases.

There is nothing more familiar and commonplace than water. However, when considered scientifically, there is nothing that offers more astonishing properties. For example, when you freeze it, its volume increases. It is the only substance on earth that will increase in volume when you change it from a liquid to a solid.

Why is it that only water has this astonishing property? The only way to answer this is to ask the Creator Himself, but there is one possibility: if we consider water from the point of view of its circulation around the earth, then perhaps it could be no other way.

All water on earth takes one of three forms: that of sea or fresh water; that of subterranean water or of vapor in clouds;

and that of a solid in glacial water. If the volume of ice were to shrink, glaciers would become heavier than water and sink to the bottom of the ocean.

If that were to happen, they could not be melted by the rays of the sun, and the temperature of the ocean would start to fall. In that case, the earth would start to freeze, and most life would perish. Moreover, the circulation of water would cease. Glaciers can be thought of as being the storehouse of the earth's water and as acting as a global thermostat. Therefore, it is necessary for them to become solids so that they can be carried by the world's oceans.

Another thing that we usually fail to realize is that the amount of water on this earth neither increases nor decreases. Looking at the big picture, mankind has forever been using the same water constantly recycled by nature.

It is this very water that we are now rapidly polluting. Water has superb solubility, so it can easily be diluted with various other substances. Thus, it ends up mixed in with agricultural and various other kinds of dangerous chemicals. In this kind of tainted water, the clusters are large. When clusters are large, permeability will suffer, and the water will not be able to fulfill its proper function.

Thinking of it in the simplest terms, we would have a situation where if such water were purified, we could drink it. However, once water has become mixed with toxic substances and the clusters have become enlarged, they cannot be so easily reduced again, even by filtration.

In the world of nature, the only time clusters are reduced in size is when water evaporates and rises. At this time, it completely casts off any dirt and becomes as pure as a newborn baby. However, the moment it turns into rain or snow and falls to earth, it very soon becomes polluted again.

You often hear it said that water has deteriorated. However, it is not simply a case of the water having become mixed with harmful or poisonous substances or having been bacterially polluted. If that were the case, we could easily purify it by simple filtration. The problem is that in coming into contact with pollutants the very clusters of the water are changed.

Not all the details are known at present, but it seems that it is not just a matter of whether the clusters are large or small: the very shape that they take must also be taken into account. To put it crudely, it would appear that it is possible that when water comes into contact with a poisonous substance, it takes on the peculiar cluster shape of that poison. If this is the case, then it may also take on the same toxic qualities of that poison as well.

If we think of it in that way, then it becomes clear that it will be no easy matter to find small cluster water in an environment that is in a state of deterioration, as at present. Perhaps it is possible to find such water in nature even now in the form of spring water, but it would not be possible to apply such water to everyday use. I suspect that the only way we might be able to obtain such small cluster water easily might be through Pi-Water.

## HIGHER CONCENTRATION DOESN'T MEAN GREATER EFFECTIVENESS

Pi-Water is mixed with ordinary water in extremely small amounts of only one or two drops at a time. Therefore, there is a tendency to try to increase Pi-Water's effectiveness by increasing the amount. However, it has become clear that increasing the concentration does not necessarily increase the effectiveness. It would appear that there is an optimum dose depending on the situation.

If you read Chapter Three on this point, I think you will see what I mean here. The reason why this should be, though, is not yet been confirmed. For example, a person with a kidney complaint drinks ten drops at a time but sees no result; another person with the same complaint takes just one drop at a time and sees an improvement.

On the other hand, sometimes it is better to drink a larger amount. In this situation, you can only the follow the advice of a physician who has real case histories on which to base his or her advice. However, as I mentioned before, whatever you do, there is nothing to fear from side effects. It is safe for you to experiment for yourselves on this point.

Basically, however, the appropriate concentration of Pi-Water will be one or two drops per cup of water. If we compare this to the amount of ordinary medicine needed to produce an effect, the amount of Pi-Water would seem to be almost nothing.

I have previously mentioned BES, UFO, and PAISEIREI in connection with Pi-Water, and these may be regarded as extracts of that substance. However, Pi-Water created from ordinary tap water using the Pi-Water Purifier should not be regarded the same as high-energy Pi-Water. In one way, such water could be seen as just ordinary water that has been purified.

It is natural that one should wonder whether such water would be effective. We, too, are unable to reach a full logical explanation of why Pi-Water should have the effect it does. Although its efficacy has been confirmed in various clinical examples, a general theory of its action has yet to be posited. We do know that one of its properties is to act as an antagonist to calcium, but this in no way fully explains its effect.

In that way, it is an extremely miraculous substance. In Chapter One, I suggested that it might work by assimilating and converting cosmic energy into bio-energy, to act as a kind of transformer. However, that is partly because there appears to be no other way to explain it.

In relation to its being effective even at low concentrations, we may find a hint in western medicine in something known as homeopathy, a kind of folk medicine. In the past, in time of plague, this kind of medicine was able to offer an unusual treatment. It is said that the stool of plague victims would be dissolved in a certain liquid. This process would be carried out again and again. The concentration would gradually reduce to one part in many millions, then one part in many tens of millions, and so on. Eventually, there would be hardly any trace of the original stool left. At this point it would be given to the patient to drink. It was found to be effective.

This resembles a kind of vaccine treatment. Why it should be that a reduced concentration of germs acts as a vaccine is still not really known. However, because of the example given above, this kind of folk homeopathy was to become very popular throughout Europe.

Personally, I believe it may have been due to the information memory ability of water. Water is able to remember information. It can remember information in the same kind of way as video or cassette tape. The stool of the plague victims would have carried information regarding the organism's fight with the plague germ. When that stool was dissolved in a certain liquid, maybe the molecules of that water were able to read and store the relevant information regarding the plague germ, white blood cells, and the body's immune system's fight against it.

There are many germs inside our bodies that are in a constant war with our immune system. If, in the end, the body loses that fight, then we die. Even in a patient who has eventually died, there must have been certain occasions when his or her immune system was able to win, and a record of that could be expected to still be there as information. Information is an essential part of water itself, so no matter how much you may dilute it, that information should still be there.

When water conveys that remembered information in some way to a living organism, it also conveys cosmic energy, thus heightening the body's natural healing power. This mechanism would appear to be naturally in-built. In other words, even without resorting to artificial medicines, there is a way to treat all sorts of natural diseases.

Regarding the appropriate concentration of Pi-Water, it would seem likely that the way water-conveyed information does its work will vary depending on the type of problem and the patient's condition. Thinking of it that way, we can get some understanding of how Pi-Water's astonishing powers work. Whatever the case, merely increasing the dosage of Pi-Water will not be enough to ensure its efficacy.

### How to use Pi-Water at different concentrations

There is some research available that gives us a good idea as to the connection between the concentration of Pi-Water and effectiveness. This research investigated the effect of high-energy Pi-Water (BES) on the activation of blood cells in rat liver cells.

Investigators observed how the index of cell activation altered at different concentrations of BES by diluting BES to a power of 10, 100, and 1000 times. The results showed that activation increased 150 times at a concentration of 10, 180 times at a concentration of 100, and 170 times at a concentration of 1000.

One might normally expect effectiveness to increase with concentration, but this turned out not to be so. With BES, the optimum concentration for effectiveness was at a concentration of 100. This would produce a stronger effect than at a concentration of even ten times higher than that amount.

This research was carried out by a lecturer at the Hamamatsu University School of Medicine, Naohiro Kanayama. If we look at the data from his work on the smooth muscle of uterus contraction, then we find that BES is most effective at a low concentration of between 0.1 and 0.3 percent. It is clear from these same data that a high concentration will have a negative influence on effectiveness.

It is important to remember this when using high-energy Pi-Water. Of course, this doesn't mean that the lower the concentration, the more effective it will always be. There will be an optimum dose for each individual.

The treatment of bedsores provides us with a clinical example to back this up. Here we have a case where UFO was used in treating long-term inpatients. Thinking that suddenly starting with an undiluted solution would be a bit too strong, investigators first tried it at a dilution of 1:50 parts, but no clear effect was seen. So, next they tried it undiluted. This time, there was a marked improvement in the patient's condition.

However, although this may have been the case in the instance of bedsores, it should not be taken as applicable to all types of problems. For example, if we look at diabetes sufferers, we find that, to a certain extent (more than 30 drops per day), the higher the concentration, the more the blood sugar drops. However, with chronic hepatitis or chronic nephritis, we find that a lower dose (less than five drops per day) will also often produce a strong effect.

I will discuss the data obtained from various clinical examples in Chapter Three. Pi-Water has the power to take cosmic energy and use it by transforming it into bio-energy. However, its effect has not been discovered to be uniform: there will be an optimum concentration value at which to maximize its effect that will depend on certain conditions. Therefore, rather than just using it once, finding no beneficial effect, and then giving up, you should experiment with various amounts for yourself.

In the process of trying out various amounts, the best concentration for you will soon make itself apparent. Let me give you some examples of results and methods of taking Pi-Water that have come from such experimentation.

- **Applying dosages for tired eyes and cataracts**
  Put just one or two drops of UFO in a 10-milliliter cup containing energy water (water from Pi-Water Purifier) and you have eye medicine that will be effective for tired eyes, cataracts, glaucoma, and various other eye complaints. It will even be effective for cases of conjunctivitis that have begun to fester.

- **Killing pain of wounds**
  If a hangnail has come off, put one drop of pure UFO onto the affected area to quell the pain.

- **Easing the pain of cancer**
  For cancer victims suffering from stomach pain, put 12 drops of BES into energy water and drink. Repeat three times. Next, put Pi-salt into hot water warmed to about 45 degrees centigrade and let it dissolve. Then add a few drops of BES and soak your ankles in it for 10 minutes, letting them warm. After that, soak them in cold water for 10 seconds. On repeating this process, the pain will subside.

(The above data are all taken from a report given by panellist, Dr.Takashi Tsurumi at the Pi-Water Symposium held at the Tokyo Big Site on the 30th of March, 1997.)

From just this one report, I think you will be able to see that there are many ways to take Pi-Water and that there is no one optimum concentration. Moreover, each individual has a different constitution. Therefore, it is best to experiment for yourself to find the best way of using Pi-Water for you. It is possible to try various methods of taking Pi-Water as it has no side effects.

### PI-WATER HOLDS THE KEY TO THE MYSTERY OF LIFE

More than 50 years have passed since World War II ended, and Japan has become a materially wealthy nation. On the other hand, though, the number of sick continues to rise. There is plenty of food available, and the level of hygiene is high. Medicine and pharmaceutics have made great strides. So why is it that the number of sick patients continues to increase? One reason clearly lies in the deterioration of the environment and our heavy reliance on dangerous chemicals.

However, this is not the whole story. There has been a fundamental misunderstanding, an illusion regarding sickness and health that has persisted for hundreds of years. I believe that unless we correct this basic mistake, we will never be able to attain real and meaningful improvements in health. I believe that in order to achieve this, we must not get too bogged down in scientific proofs. We must be prepared to look the evidence before our eyes squarely in the face.

The illusion, the big misunderstanding into which we have fallen, is the idea of the omnipotence of science. If something cannot be measured by scientific means, we consider it to be unknowable. Could not denying the existence of the unmeasurable be a big mistake? Right now, science only understands one small part of the way the cosmos, the earth, nature itself works.

To give an extreme example, if we put just one grain of crystal rock sugar into our mouth, we have no idea what will happen to it in the future. There are some things that we do know, but to take that small piece of knowledge and then maintain we know everything is, I believe, a big mistake.

However, modern man, used to scientific thinking, believes he now knows everything. It is rather like looking at someone's resume and thinking you then know everything about that person. I feel that modern man is running a great risk by regarding science in this way.

Making people realize that mistake or, to put it another way, finding new evidence that would serve to make people make a fundamental reappraisal of science has not been easy. It would appear that only recently, little by little, a new understanding is dawning in various fields.

One such piece of evidence is the new knowledge brought to us by the science of genetic engineering. I believe that the knowledge such science is now bringing to us is revolutionary in its implications: it has taught us that the traditional view of life as being irreplaceable, a one time only event, is not the whole story. It is a little more complex than that. If we take the case of human beings, it has been believed that the brain played a pivotal role and that it holds the key to everything (this is why we have the line of reasoning that holds that brain death constitutes death). However, the fact is that life is not single-, but dual-structured.

What exactly does this mean? The human body is made up of a conglomeration of cells that form the living organism.

However, cells have their own unique life pattern, too. Each cell is trying to lead a life of its own. So what is the "volition" of the cell? It is by no means the support of the organism to which that cell belongs.

A cancer cell is a typical example of this idea. In order to preserve its own life, a cancer cell will proceed to destroy the larger organism to which it belongs. It could probably be said that many illnesses are, in the final analysis, a result of this conflict between a cell trying to preserve its own life and the interests of the larger organism to which it belongs. And the cause of this conflict can be found in external factors like stress, poor diet, exposure to chemicals, and a poor environment.

Pi-Water may act to alleviate this conflict between individual cells and the larger grouping of cells that make up the living organism. I believe it is possible to think of Pi-Water in this way. In any case, as I will show from Chapter Three onward, Pi-Water has astonishing powers. And there is no way that the fact of these powers can be denied.

We will not be abandoning the pursuit of science, but, at a time when concern about health continues to grow, I believe that the wonderful results obtained in treatment under the direction of various specialists should be widely known. The appropriate significance should also be attributed to these results. Apart from that, everything will depend on how you, the reader, make use of it yourselves.

# CHAPTER THREE

❁ ❁ ❁

# CANCER AND VARIOUS LIFESTYLE RELATED DISEASES: HOW PI-WATER CAN HELP

## DRAMATIC IMPROVEMENT IN CONDITION OF PATIENT ON KIDNEY MACHINE

In this chapter, I would like to report about the effect of Pi-Water in cases of cancer and various other lifestyle related diseases, giving a number of clinical examples and instances as related by sufferers themselves. First, let us look at kidney disease. The following gives an example of this.

The patient is a 23-year-old man with a four-year history of a chronic kidney disorder, who was undergoing dialysis on a kidney machine three times a week.

Dialysis was scheduled for Mondays, Wednesdays, and Fridays, so there was a gap over the weekend. His body was unable to adjust over this break, so he was in considerable discomfort. Another patient suffering from the same problem told him, "I started to drink energy water, and now I feel much better." So he, too, bought a water purifier and began drinking water from it.

At the same time, he also used UFO. On so doing, the increase in his body weight that would occur on a Monday (urine unable to leave the body will cause it to swell and will increase body weight) reduced by as much as half. Dialysis became much less of an ordeal compared than before, and his physician was amazed.

In another case, on taking UFO, a 52-year-old female patient suffering from the same disease maintained that on the seventh day she was able to lose the sensation of itching that had continually plagued her for some five years.

Again, there is the case of another male patient in his 40s who had undergone dialysis for five years. Blood tests showed that he was in very poor condition and that both his red and white blood cell values were half those of a normal healthy individual. He, too, purchased a water purifier and began to drink energy water. About one month later, he was able to urinate forcefully. Furthermore, his red blood cell value increased from 185 to 285, and his white blood cell value increased from 2,500 to 5,300. This is quite a spectacular improvement in both values.

The kidneys serve to filter the blood and produce urine. Nephritis is a kidney problem caused when the glomerulus, a cluster of the kidney's filtering blood vessels, becomes inflamed. It will cause a number of problems such as swelling, urinary complications, high blood pressure, and so on. As it progresses, it becomes incurable. When the function of the kidneys is impaired up to a certain point, the condition degenerates into kidney failure.

It is an extremely serious problem, and once the kidneys are no longer able to filter the blood, the patient is in serious trouble. If he or she doesn't receive artificial dialysis, the patient will die. So what effect does Pi-Water have on this particular disease?

From the examples I have given above, those of chronic nephritis and kidney failure, it can be seen that Pi-Water is effective in such cases. However, these accounts provide us with no empirical evidence. Therefore, let me go on to introduce some clinical examples of the use of BES.

According to research carried out by the Middle-to-Old Aged Health Research Society ("Investigation into the Effects of BES on Various Illnesses"), both the pain and numbness often experienced by patients with chronic kidney failure undergoing dialysis were found to be alleviated on taking BES. When this effect appeared was rather spread out, but in faster cases an improvement could be seen within one week. Even slower cases could expect some kind of improvement within one month.

To investigate its diuretic properties, investigators gave patients with a daily urinary output of less than 200 milliliters six drops of BES per day over a two-month period. Although no change was seen in the amount of urine produced, there was an improvement in the patients' ability to expel gas and produce sweat.

If we combine these results with patients' own accounts of improvements in urinary output, we can see that Pi-Water is effective as a diuretic. Moreover, looking at these examples and various other clinical research data, I feel it would be correct to consider Pi-Water as being effective in improving symptoms in chronic nephritis and kidney failure patients who are undergoing dialysis.

### TEST VALUES IN HEPATITIS SHOW MARKED IMPROVEMENT

Now let's look at the effect of Pi-Water on liver conditions. The liver has been called the silent organ. While fulfilling the most functions of any of the body's organs, unlike the stomach, it goes about its work quietly, often not giving pain and drawing attention to itself. Unless the deterioration is quite serious, the patient doesn't realize that there is a problem at all, and when he does, it is too late to do anything about it.

Among liver complaints, the most serious is viral hepatitis. This particular infection spreads through contact with blood or bodily fluids and has been known to be passed on during blood transfusions (Hepatitis B and C). Hepatitis A, moreover, can be passed on through drink or foodstuffs. Often, it will not be the patient's own fault. If you are infected, there is no other way to regard it except as just bad luck. This type of viral hepatitis is widespread at the moment. Therefore, let me introduce a few clinical examples of the use of Pi-Water in cases of hepatitis.

First let's look at its effect on Hepatitis C. The first case is a patient who showed a remarkable recovery from Hepatitis C on taking UFO. (This was the case of Emeritus Professor, Shigetoshi Shiota of Tokyo Medical and Dental University.)

> I had received a blood transfusion during surgery some 25 years previously, and when I had my yearly general checkup in 1982, my GOT and GPT were found to have risen from 14 and 13 to 31 and 37, respectively, from the previous year. The following year, these values rose to 84 and 188, and I was diagnosed as having fatty liver. Later, it was ascertained that it was not Hepatitis A or B. My GPT remained at around the 100 level, reaching 210 for a short time. However, after that, the highest value was

near 100, with the lowest peaking throughout the rest of the year at 50 and 60. During this time, I continued to receive powerful intravenous shots of Minophagen C.

In April of 1996, my GPT was 85, and in May it was 88. On the 31st of May my GOT was 74, and my GPT had risen to 101. Therefore, on consultation with Dr. Kenji Hashimoto of Hamamatsu University School of Medicine, it was decided to try Pi-Water. The physicians decided to use it in conjunction with 100 milligrams, three times per day, of ursodesoxycholic acid, something to disperse any toxins and stimulate liver function.

Every morning, I would drink one cup of milk containing 10 drops of UFO. A test on the 14th of June showed that my GPT had dramatically fallen to a value of 28. Moreover, in July, my GPT had fallen to 8. After that, it remained between 6 and 11. And my gamma-GPT, which had shown a highest value of 148, fell to 10. My blood platelets also showed a normal value of 210,000.

Furthermore, from the 12th of May, 1997, instead of milk, they started using Pi-Water from the purifier containing 10 drops of UFO.

In a test given on April of 1997, I was found to have negative Hepatitis C antigens in a quantitative and qualitative analysis (by the RT-PCR of HCV-RNA method). My HCV antibodies showed a value of 3, and my RDR-A gave a reading of 2 (up to 0.9). My antibody value, too, showed a gradual decrease. My blood platelets were normal, and an ultrasonic scan showed no abnormalities in my liver.

My hepatitis was considered to have been cured, as I was able to maintain the same kind of results in further tests for over a year after that.

Here, I would like to describe a little about the way my chronic hepatitis was dealt with.

Currently, the only medicine that offers any hope of a cure for chronic hepatitis is interferon, but this, too, has its limitations. Side effects can be a problem, and there is an age limit at which it can be used. The same kind of problems may be found with most medicines, so really it becomes a matter of a fight between the illness and your own willpower. What is important is that you:

1. Lead a well-regulated life, keeping regular hours and habits. After meals, it is important to lie down and keep quiet for between 30 minutes to one hour in order not to put a strain on your liver (the blood flow in your liver will increase by some 30 percent if you lie down).
2. Take moderate exercise. With chronic hepatitis there will be a continuous inflammation of the liver. That is to say there will be a localized circulatory problem. Therefore, anything that will improve blood circulation is beneficial. It is believed that moderate walking will help the blood circulate well throughout the body. The best time to walk is apparently very early in the morning before any food intake, as this will put the minimum strain on the liver. On leaving the house at 6 am, I take ten drops of UFO and walk 3,500 meters, adding some movements from the radio exercise program halfway. Walking, then, serves to improve the circulation of the blood through the liver, thereby helping to circulate the UFO in the liver.
3. Take care to follow an appropriate diet to your problem. Try to eat high-protein and high-calorie food. No alcohol. Consume as much milk, cheese, tofu, and as many potatoes of any kind as possible. Standing and eating at the same time will put a strain on the liver and so should be avoided.

Thus, I experienced a miraculous cure of a chronic Hepatitis C that had plagued me for 15 years by using UFO and Uruso in conjunction with powerful Minophagen C.

(The above is an extract from the 1998 Spring edition of *Pi-Tech Forum*, a journal published by the Association for Research and Propagation of Bio Energy Systems.)

The next case concerns a 55-year-old woman suffering from chronic Hepatitis C. She took two drops of BES every day for two months. Her test values then showed she had showed improvement as follows:

Main test values before and after medication (figures in parantheses show normal values)

GOT: 85 (8-40)→57
GPT: 147(5-40)→79
gamma-GTP: 36(0-40)→19
ZTT: 13.1(4-12)→12
TTT: 3.5(1.5-7.0)→3.7

As you can see from these results, GOT and GPT failed to reach normal values but managed to show a marked improvement. In order to ascertain whether this was due to the effect of BES, treatment was temporarily suspended, and tests were carried out once again one month later. The values that had only just shown an improvement were found to have returned to their former state:

GOT: 57→87
GPT: 79→130
gamma-GTP: 19→40
ZTT: 12.0→15.3
TTT: 3.7→5.2

The earlier improvement had been completely reversed, so treatment with BES was resumed. On so doing, after two months, all the values began to show an improvement. After 11 months, GOT was 55 (down from 85), GPT was 78 (down from 147), gamma-GTP was 21 (down from 36), ZTT was 14.8 (up from 13.1), and TTT was 4.6 (up from 3.5).

There are many other clinical examples of Hepatitis C showing such marked improvement in test values. I will just note the main points:

- **Hepatitis C (49-year-old woman)**
  She took 10 drops of BES daily, and after one month all her test values showed an improvement. However, at the sixth month, all her values suddenly worsened as she had overdone it at work and tired herself out. Later, though, at the eighth month, all her values improved: GOT to 216 (307 at the sixth month), GPT to 290 (410 previously), gamma-GTP to 52 (70), ZTT to 33.1 (33.6), and TTT to 17.4 (15.6).
- **Hepatitis C (45-year-old man)**
  On taking four drops of BES per day, after one month his values were: GOT to 83 (down from 88), GPT to 143 (down from 155), gamma-GTP to 75 (down from 87), and ZTT to 14 (12.6). In this case, his liver function showed a marked improvement.
- **Hepatitis B (50-year-old man)**
  He had been diagnosed with Hepatitis B ten years previously, and it had become chronic. He took 36 drops of BES per day (12 drops, three times per day) along with Chinese herbal medicine. At the 22nd month, the following test values were obtained showing a marked improvement: GOT to 30 (down from 86), and GPT to 14 (down from 40).

I believe it could be said that it is clear from these results that BES is extremely effective in improving liver function. Bearing this in mind, please read the following accounts from a 38-year-old sufferer himself. I'm sure you will realize that his experience cannot just be attributed to his not being a medical expert:

> I had suffered from chronic hepatitis for four years and whiplash syndrome for three years. As a result, I continuously felt numb and was easily tired. An acquaintance

recommended Pi-Water to me, so everyday I would drink three cups. I used to carry a one-liter bottle wherever I went, even to work. On so doing, at the end of the first week, I experienced diarrhea, chest pains, and headaches.

However, I had been warned to expect something like that, so I stuck to it and kept on drinking. One week later, I felt thoroughly invigorated, through and through. Currently, I'm at the end of the third month. Even my constipation has gone away. I can hardly believe that I actually have hepatitis.

### TOWARD A CURE FOR DANGEROUS DIABETES IN ONLY TWO AND A HALF MONTHS

Pi-Water has also been shown to be remarkably effective against diabetes. Let me tell you about someone I know. The president of a certain company, well into his 60s, he had led an extremely healthy and active life. Then, suddenly he felt dizzy one day; he visited a hospital and was found to have high blood pressure.

On further examination, it turned out that he had diabetes, and it was this that was driving up his blood pressure. The doctor gave him several medications including drugs for his diabetes, something to reduce his blood pressure, vitamins, and so on. I bumped into him on his way back from the hospital and on hearing his story recommended Pi-Water.

The problem is that people who don't know anything about it tend to regard Pi-Water as nothing more than "just water." My acquaintance, too, apparently at first thought, "If we could be cured just by drinking water, we'd all be happy. We could do away with doctors and medicine altogether!"

However, he was also a little bit uneasy about the number of drugs he had received from his doctor. I told him that the reason I had recommended Pi-Water was that I actually knew someone with diabetes who had taken it and that that person had experienced a remarkable improvement in his health.

He thought about it for a while and then announced that he would drink it for one week and see. So, he began taking PAISEIREI in mineral water at a dosage of 20 drops, three times per day: on arising, within 30 minutes of eating lunch, and before bed.

However, he began to worry about not taking the medicine he had been given by his doctor and started testing his own urine with a test kit. By the end of the second day, he could see no improvement whatsoever. There was still sugar in his urine.

He found the same results on the third and fourth days, too. "I knew it would be no good!" he thought. But he had promised to continue for one week, so he did, and on the morning of the fifth day he tested his urine as usual. This time, the paper that is used in such test kits (dyed green) showed no change in color. This meant that there was no sugar in his urine.

For one month after that, while still drinking PAISEIREI, he continued to keep a record of his urine test results. Although there was the occasional sugar reaction, for the most part the urine tests showed a pattern of no sugar. A hospital test then showed his blood sugar value to be 116. The normal value on an empty stomach is 70-110. This means that his value had almost returned to normal.

The doctor in charge of his case was surprised but said, "The medicine they are producing now is really good. That and looking after your health certainly work, don't they? Keep it up!" He was obviously delighted with the result and proceeded to give him another prescription for medicine, yet again.

The test results on his first visit to the hospital showed his empty stomach blood sugar value to be 311, neutral fat to be 264, and his hemoglobin A1c 12.3. He continued to take PAISEIREI for two months following that and then returned to the hospital once again for tests. This time his values were: blood sugar to 96, neutral fat to 66 (normal value: 50-120),

## Testing results - Mr. Y.S., 64 years, male, diabetes

| Test | Reference Normal Range | Unit | Test Value Before UFO Administration (July 14, 1994) | ↑↓ | Test Value after UFO Administration (October 6, 1994) | ↑↓ |
|---|---|---|---|---|---|---|
| Serum total protein | 6.5~8.4 | g/dl | 7.3 | N | 6.8 | N |
| Total CHO | 130~220 | mg/dl | 160 | N | 140 | N |
| HDL-C | 36.0~71.0 | mg/dl | 26.8 | ↓ | 31.5 | ↓ |
| RF value | 2.63~7.33 | | 5.97 | N | 4.44 | N |
| Neutral fat | 40~145 | mg/dl | 264 | ↑ | 66 | N |
| GOT | 0~40 | KU | 25 | N | 17 | N |
| GPT | 0~35 | KU | 18 | N | 13 | N |
| γ-GTP | 0~50 | IU/l | 12 | N | 7 | N |
| Serum AMY | 60~160 | UNIT | 66 | N | | |
| Creatinine | 0.7~1.5 | mg/dl | 1.6 | ↑ | 1.5 | N |
| Uric acid | 3.5~7.9 | mg/dl | 6.1 | N | 5.7 | N |
| Sodium | 135.0~147.0 | mEq/l | 138.1 | N | | |
| Potassium | 3.50~5.50 | mEq/l | 4.21 | N | | |
| Chloride | 98.0~108.0 | mEq/l | 98.1 | N | | |
| Calcium | 8.5~11.0 | mg/dl | 9.7 | N | | |
| Glucose (fasting) | 60~110 | mg/dl | 311 | ↑ | 96 | N |
| HbA1C | 5.3~7.0 | % | 12.3 | ↑ | 7.4 | ↑ |
| Fructosan | 200~300 | umol/l | 590 | ↑ | 268 | N |

Note: N indicates normal value.

hemoglobin A1c to 7.4. All of the values had shown a remarkable improvement. It could probably said that his recovery was all due to PAISEIREI. (Table on page 55.)

Here are a number of clinical examples:

- **Diabetes (39-year-old woman)**
  "My doctor recommended insulin, but I wasn't happy with the idea and went to another hospital where they gave me BES. Along with something to get my blood sugar down (one tablet per day), I took 45 drops of BES per day. Before taking BES, my empty stomach blood sugar value was 336. But, after three and a half months on BES, it improved, falling to 190. That's a little above the normal value, but I continued to take it as before and kept on improving."

- **Diabetes (55-year-old man)**
  This man also suffered from high blood pressure. He took 27 drops of BES per day along with some Chinese herbal medicine (Hange-shashin-to). Approximately one month later, he took a test and his values were found to be: empty stomach blood sugar to 80 (down from 131), urine sugar to minus (from plus), and blood pressure to 126 over 88 (down from 142 over 88). All had shown an improvement.

- **Diabetes (60-year-old woman)**
  This woman also exhibited high blood pressure as a complication. She took 36 drops of BES per day along with Chinese herbal medicine (Hochu-ekki-to). Her test values at one month later showed: empty stomach blood sugar to 87 (down from 287) and blood pressure at 123 over 74 (down from 143 over 76). All had shown a remarkable improvement.

### DOCTORS, TOO, SEE REMARKABLE RESULTS IN DIABETES

We have also received many reports of personal experience of improvements in diabetes from people using energy water and UFO. Let me go on to introduce a few of these:

- **Diabetes (28-year-old woman)**
  "I have had diabetes for 15 years. I had only been going to get a blood test two or three times a year. So after starting to take UFO, I began to go once a month to see whether it was working. Since then, over the last five months, the doctor has told me that all my test values are normal.
  "They say that if these results are unsatisfactory, you can get all sorts of complications, such as eye problems, nervous problems, and so on. But now I have no complications whatsoever, and I'm able to lead a perfectly normal life, just like a healthy person."

- **Diabetes (65-year-old woman)**
  "I had a high blood sugar count and was attending a hospital, but nothing seemed to change, either for the better or the worse. I heard about Pi-Water from an acquaintance, and more for the sake of the health of my family than for myself, I bought a purifier.
  "I drank energy water for a while and then went back to the hospital. The doctor was full of praise, saying, 'You really have been trying hard, haven't you?' which was rather surprising considering that, apart from drinking energy water, I hadn't been doing anything in particular.
  "The only thing I had been doing was to drink two liters of energy water every day. Apparently, to get any effect from energy water, you need to drink between 1.5 and 2 liters per day. I've got a bad back, so usually I have had to hold on to the rail when I climb the stairs at the subway station. But then I suddenly realized I was able to walk straight up the middle without holding on!"

- **Diabetes (61-year-old woman)**
  "Since becoming an inpatient with diabetes some three years ago, I had found getting up in the morning hard, and it would often take me as long as 15 minutes. But, since starting to drink energy water, I have been able to practi-

cally jump out of bed. Moreover, people often comment on how good my complexion has become.

"At the moment, I have my own original fruit juice that I make to maintain my health. The recipe: first I soak some vegetables such as beefsteak plant, felon herb, sunflower, field horsetail, cabbage, spinach, and so on in energy water and remove any residue from them. Then, I put in banana and apple and mix it all together. Next, I add honey or brown sugar to taste. Finally, I put in a measure of energy water, and it's ready. I had been doing this for some time with ordinary tap water, and it hadn't been so nice to taste or smell. But since changing over to Pi-Water, I've been happily able to go on drinking it, and my health has got much better, too."

- **Diabetes (63-year-old man)**
"Before I started drinking Pi-Water, my blood sugar value (on an empty stomach) was 125, and my blood pressure was 140 over 90. My heart and lungs were a mess. If I breathed any cold air, I would start to have problems. Walking, too, could only be done with difficulty.

"Moreover, if I walked with a stoop, I would soon get chest pains, and as soon as I started to get tired my back would begin to hurt. But I've noticed that all these problems have improved since I got the Pi-Water Purifier and started drinking energy water.

"My blood sugar is 118, close to the normal value, and my blood pressure has fallen to 110 at its highest. I am convinced that it can only get better."

- **Diabetes (33-year-old man)**
"I remember I had stomach ulcers and had to have four fifths of my stomach surgically removed. They told me at the time that my blood sugar value was high, and I was diagnosed as diabetic. At that time, my blood sugar value was an astonishing 600.

"So I was re-admitted to hospital, this time for treatment of diabetes. As soon as there was an improvement, I would be released. When it got worse, I would be re-admitted. This was the pattern that was repeated again and again. At that point, someone introduced me to the Pi-Water Purifier, saying that it was good for improving diabetes.

"I got one as soon as possible. As I began to feel better, I also started to take UFO. On taking UFO, both my blood sugar value and blood pressure started to show a remarkable fall, coming within a hair's breadth of the normal value."

### *Treatment without using insulin*

Patients with advanced diabetes are given insulin for their condition. It is considered to be difficult to reduce dosage or suspend insulin treatment in such patients. However, at the Suzuki Clinic of Internal Medicine in Hamamatsu (Head of Hospital: Hideki Suzuki), there have been a number of instances where a complete cure has been effected, or where they have been able to suspend insulin treatment by using high-energy Pi-Water in conjunction with other treatment.

## PI-WATER WORKS TO NORMALIZE BLOOD PRESSURE

High blood pressure in itself is not a disease, but it can cause the onset of a number of other diseases. It seems that Pi-Water works to lower blood pressure when it is too high and raise blood pressure when it is too low.

High blood pressure is defined as any value above the normal range of 95 at its lowest to 160 at its highest. If blood pressure remains higher than this normal value for any length of time, then it can cause the blood flow to be impeded and contribute to problems with brain, heart, kidney function, and so on. Finally, it can lead to various problems such as brain infarctions, subarachnoid hemorrhages, angina, and sclerosis of the kidneys.

Nobody really knows what causes high blood pressure, but it is more likely to occur if it runs in the family. There does appear to be a genetic factor involved. Obesity, too, can be a factor. People with diabetes, heavy drinkers, those who overwork, these are all possible candidates. It is even said that overconsumption of very salty food could be involved.

Currently, it is estimated that there are approximately 20 million Japanese with high blood pressure. This means that some 20 million people have the likelihood of developing a high blood pressure related adult disease at some time or other. How drinking Pi-Water can markedly reduce blood pressure has clearly been confirmed from a number of clinical examples.

A 60-year-old man with a blood pressure reading of 178 over 106 began taking 36 drops of BES per day. After approximately two months, his pressure fell to 139 over 84. This is perfectly within the normal range.

A 51-year-old woman with a blood pressure reading of 182 over 100 took 27 drops of BES per day. In a short period of time her blood pressure fell to 148 over 68.

Low blood pressure, on the other hand, is often thought of as not being such a problem. However, it is just as bad as high blood pressure and can lead to a number of problems. Low blood pressure is generally considered to be any value below 100 at its highest. Sufferers tend to tire easily. They often get headaches, dizziness, stiff shoulders, palpitations, constipation, and various digestion related illnesses. Finally, there is the danger that they will develop many of the same adult diseases as sufferers of high blood pressure.

Just as with high blood pressure, it is important to keep a close watch on low blood pressure. At the moment, there is no effective medicine to treat either problem. Certainly, relying solely on medicine for either is a mistake. The reason for this is that blood pressure usually adjusts itself to the needs of the moment.

For example, even a person without high blood pressure will see a rise in value to that of a person with the condition under conditions of extreme stress. There are even people who, on being told that they should have their blood pressure taken by their doctor, see that value rise.

Basically, blood pressure should be left to adjust itself to the needs of the moment. However, if you use something like a medicine to reduce blood pressure, it will take it down too far, and this can easily have a negative effect on the body as a whole. If blood pressure rises to the point where it becomes dangerous, then one must do something to bring it down. But, as far as possible, it is best to let this happen naturally. With that in mind, it could be said that it is best to take Pi-Water in order to maintain normal blood pressure on an ordinary basis.

So how does Pi-Water achieve this effect? The actual mechanism of how Pi-Water works is not yet fully understood, but, as I tried to explain in Chapter One, it is clear that it has something to do with its ability as an antagonist to the effects of calcium. Its mechanism seems to be that when it acts as an antagonist to calcium, the arteries are widened and blood pressure is decreased.

We have received reports of personal experience of normalizing blood pressure including the following experience of a 65-year-old man:

"For a long time, I had found it very difficult to get up in the morning, as I suffer from low blood pressure. My body always felt numb, and I couldn't think straight. That's the state I was in when I started drinking energy water. Since then, you wouldn't recognize me! I fairly leap out of bed, wide awake. I feel great.

"On the other hand, my wife has high blood pressure and has been seeing a doctor for some ten years or more. She, too, began drinking energy water. The doctor said, 'That's amazing! Your blood pressure is perfectly normal.' She was delighted.

"I thought I knew how important water was, but I really had no idea of how powerful energy water was. Up until now, in order to fight both low and high blood pressure, we had to be really careful about everything we ate. But now, we don't have to worry about that. It has made a big difference."

## EFFECT ON VARIOUS TYPES OF HEART DISEASE

Heart disease ranks number two after cancer as the leading cause of death in Japan. The two most representative heart problems are angina and infarctions. Angina occurs when the flow of blood into the coronary arteries, which supply the heart muscle with nourishment, is obstructed in some way. The victim will then suffer an angina attack accompanied by spasms and pain. Infarctions indicate that the heart muscle is being destroyed because the coronary arteries have become blocked.

The heart is a vital circulatory organ that acts to supply nourishment and oxygen to the body by maintaining blood flow. Even if the situation isn't critical yet, if the heart is in poor condition, then it is quite normal to see problems manifesting themselves elsewhere in the body. The stress and dietary habits of modern life tend to increase the incidence of heart disease, and it is not surprising to hear of young men in their prime suddenly dropping dead.

Pi-Water counteracts some of the problems that lead to heart disease and as a result lessens the likelihood of it occurring. For example, on drinking Pi-Water, people with obesity problems will begin to return to a normal weight. This is because it stimulates the body's metabolism and helps expel neutral fat and cholesterol from the body. As a result, this makes it useful in the prevention of various types of circulatory related problems.

Let me give you two cases of personal experience of the good effect of Pi-Water on heart disease:

- **Improvement in heart disease (66-year-old woman)**

  "I had had chronic heart disease for some time. I also used to have high blood pressure, and I often got palpitations. I had glaucoma, so my field of vision used to be very narrow. It was very difficult for me. Even if I was careful not to overdo it, I would get dizzy spells. It was like that every day. It was really terrible. Thanks to Pi-Water, all that changed.

"As soon as I got the Pi-Water Purifier and started drinking energy water, I felt like my heart was working much better, much more easily. My doctor said, 'You appear to be much better these days. Your blood pressure is down. Keep taking it easy.' I was really pleased.

"Even my palpitations, which used to just hit me out of nowhere, have subsided. I don't have to worry about them any more. Well, if it's this good, I thought, why not try it for my eyes, too? So, I started washing my eyes in energy water, and I can now see much better than before. Even my dizzy spells have completely disappeared."

- **Improvement in heart disease (two-year-old girl)**
  "At her one-month checkup, I was told that my baby daughter had a hole in her heart. I was really worried about what was the best thing to do. An acquaintance suggested I should try giving her UFO, so I started right away. I didn't think for one moment that the hole would close up, but, as a mother, I was willing to try anything that might help with the weakness in her heart.

  "Apart from UFO, I also gave her energy water. Thanks to that, her problem completely cleared up, and she was able to grow up just fine. When she was two and a half, I took her to the hospital again for a checkup. This time they said, 'We can't hear any abnormalities in her heart.' It wasn't a full checkup, but I believe the problem she had as a baby has probably been cured."

### COLON CANCER: PREVENTING ITS SPREAD, STOPPING ITS PROGRESS

Since the end of World War II, the Japanese diet has become westernized, and this has caused a remarkable increase in the incidence of cancer of the colon. Cancer of the colon can take the form of either rectal cancer or cancer of the colon itself. This type of cancer will be accompanied by stomach pain, constipation, diarrhea, bloody stool, and so on. From middle age onward, if your stomach tends to swell often, if your stool becomes thinner, or if your stomach often feels strange, then you need to consider the possibility of colon cancer.

If you continue to drink Pi-Water, you will have regular stools, and the good bacteria in your colon will be protected. Therefore, the colon as a whole will be healthier. The modern Japanese diet is meat based and is thus high in fat and protein. However, protein easily degenerates and in so doing creates toxins inside the colon. It is suspected that this might be the trigger for such cancer.

Compared to certain other types of cancer, colon cancer, if detected early enough, is relatively easy to treat. But if it metastasizes or if general degeneration of the colon occurs, it is believed that it can lead to other types of cancer. Thus, it is important to prevent the colon from getting into such a condition.

If we look at colon cancer sufferers who have been given high-energy Pi-Water BES, we find that metastasis has been checked, progression has been halted, symptoms have been improved, and so on—all the results one might expect. Let us look at some of the main points in some clinical cases:

- **Colon cancer (50-year-old man)**
  This man had received surgery for colon cancer half a year previously. It had metastasized to his liver, and he was taking anticancer drugs. He was taking 54 drops of BES daily: 18 drops three times per day. At the same time, he was taking Chinese herbal medicine (Hochu-keishi-to) and was receiving immune lymphocyte treatment. One month after beginning to use BES, he experienced a decrease in his symptoms of general pain and numbness.

- **Colon cancer (54-year-old woman)**
  In this case, the colon cancer had spread to the peritoneum. She took 54 drops of BES daily three times a day as above. At the same time, she was taking Chinese herbal medicine (Hochu-ekki-to). One and a half years after beginning BES,

a complete halt in the progress of her cancer was observed, with a clean bill of health for her blood, lymph nodes, and liver.

- **Colon cancer (75-year-old woman)**
  In this case, her colon cancer had spread to her liver and she was taking anticancer drugs. She took 54 drops of BES per day along with Chinese herbal medicine (Hochu-ekki-to). In addition to this, she was also receiving immune lymph therapy. This woman experienced quite a dramatic improvement in symptoms. Moreover, in this instance it was considered that the immune-lymph therapy and BES were incompatible.

  Apart from the above, another case had high blood pressure as a complication along with the cancer. This person took 45 drops of BES per day along with Chinese herbal medicine (Hange-shashin-to). On so doing, even after three months, no metastasis of cancer was seen. Moreover, the upper high blood pressure value dropped more than 20 points and both stiffness of the shoulders and fatigue decreased.

### IMPROVEMENT IN STOMACH CANCER: NUMBER 1 CANCER AMONG JAPANESE

There have been a number of clinical examples of Pi-Water proving effective in combating stomach cancer. Stomach cancer is the most common form of cancer among Japanese people. Recently, cases of colon cancer have been rising sharply, but stomach cancer still continues to claim more lives than any other type of cancer (one in four deaths from cancer are attributable to stomach cancer).

A number of causes have been attributed to stomach cancer such as over-salty food, overstimulation of the stomach from polluted chemical substances, and food additives. It could be said that everyone is in danger from stomach cancer as stress, too, poses a threat.

Let's look at two clinical cases of stomach cancer:

- **Stomach cancer (67-year-old man)**
  This man had undergone surgery for his stomach cancer, but, on opening his stomach, the physicians found that the cancer had spread too much and closed him up without removing the cancer. This is a case where BES was another option. He took 54 drops of BES along with Chinese herbal medicine. Four months after beginning BES, he experienced a complete relief from pain, and it is believed that his cancer may either have been stopped or that improvement may have occurred.

- **Stomach cancer (64-year-old man)**
  This man had received a stomach camera test at hospital and had been found to have stomach ulcers. Examination of the ulcer tissue led to a diagnosis of Class 5 cancer. He took 27 drops of BES per day, taking no other medication whatsoever. Six months after beginning BES, he took a stomach camera test again, this time at a different hospital. No cancer was found. He reported this to the previous hospital and was tested again. The finding of no cancer was confirmed.

It can be seen from the above two clinical examples that Pi-Water has a remarkable effect on stomach cancer. There are some extremely interesting personal reports of improvements in stomach cancer from people who have taken UFO and energy water rather than BES, too. I will now describe two such examples:

- **Stomach cancer (72-year-old man)**
  "I had an ulcerated stomach and had to have two thirds of it removed under surgery. Ten years later, I had stomach problems again and had to go back for more surgery. This time they removed an ulcer the size of a fist. Tests showed that it contained innumerable cancer cells. They told me that it had spread to my other organs and that, 'You only have three months to live.'

"Two months later I found out about UFO and started drinking it. Five days later the numbness and pain in my hands and legs started to subside, and the color in both hands returned to a healthy normal. When my three months were up, I went back to the hospital for a CT scan. This time, they told me that the spread of the cancer had been stopped.

"Two months later, I went back for a second CT scan. It was confirmed that my cancer had improved even more, and the doctor said, 'How could this have happened?' Later, I regained a normal level of strength and a vigorous appetite. I still can't believe I am a man who had been told he had terminal cancer."

- **Stomach cancer (27-year-old woman)**

  "My aunt developed stomach cancer some 20 years ago. Although the ulceration in her stomach had settled down, of recent years, each summer the ulcers have returned, getting worse. On top of this, she developed Basedow's disease, and she was in great distress with the pain from her stomach and back. However, thanks to Pi-Water, they say her ulcers have cleared up.

  "They tested her again with the stomach camera but found no sign whatsoever of ulcers in the three places they'd been found before. My aunt had been taking UFO and energy water. My father-in-law had gone into hospital with cirrhosis, so we immediately got him to take it, too. His condition had been up and down, but now it showed such an improvement that he was eventually able to leave hospital. The doctor was astounded."

### ADVANCED LUNG CANCER: IN RETREAT IN SIX MONTHS

Lung cancer, too, has been rising in recent years. When you say lung cancer, most people immediately think of tobacco. However, even nonsmokers aren't safe from this disease as it can be triggered by a number of other factors such as atmospheric pollution, carcinogenic chemical substances, diet, nutrition, and so on. We call it lung cancer in general, but there are actually many types: cancer of the upper epidermis, small-cell cancer, large-cell cancer, glandular cancer, and so on. Recently, glandular cancer has been on the increase in Japan. It is said that this type of cancer has no particular relation to smoking.

Moreover, lung cancer can sometimes result from metastasis from other cancers. One man was given six months to live by his doctor after contracting a lung cancer that had spread from his tongue. He was still only in his 50s. He tried anticancer drugs, but they were almost totally ineffective. He continued to suffer from low fevers, a cough, and headaches, and eventually the cancer started to spread to his lymph glands.

The doctor said, "You will experience difficulty in breathing within one to two weeks." At this time, he happened to learn about UFO, and partly to ease his mind he began taking it. Until then, he had been hospitalized. Apparently, when he started drinking UFO, the doctor let him go home, saying, "You can spend your last days at home." However, his condition gradually began to improve. Ten days after leaving hospital he had an X-ray, and although no change was to be seen in the size of his tumor, his chest pains, headaches, cough, and so on all showed a clear improvement. The doctor said, "You have got your strength back" and began a course of radiotherapy. They were worried about side effects, but these have turned out to be much less than imagined. He has been able to lead a fairly normal life while fighting this disease. What the final result will be, we don't yet know. However, it is certain that Pi-Water acts to improve the symptoms peculiar to lung cancer sufferers and to lighten the terrible side effects that can occur with drastic treatments such as radiotherapy. It would seem probable that if you could more easily withstand such side effects, then your chances of recovery would be accordingly higher.

There have been a number of clinical reports, too, of BES causing a retreat in cases of lung cancer. Let's take the case of one 70-year-old man who had been told he had lung cancer. He was given anticancer drugs and radiotherapy. His cancer was already fairly advanced, and by the time he began taking BES he was already considered last stage.

In this case, the patient began by taking 45 drops of BES per day along with Chinese herbal medicine (Seiko-keishi-to). On this treatment alone, six months later he had an X-ray. This confirmed that his tumor had begun to shrink. His symptoms had also subsided.

### LIVER CANCER CURED WITHOUT SURGERY AND WITHOUT DRUGS!

It is said that liver cancer can be triggered by chronic viral hepatitis. Naturally, we can predict that an increase in cases of viral hepatitis can lead to an increase in cases of liver cancer. In fact, next to stomach and lung cancer, liver cancer is the most prevalent in Japan.

One patient who had chronic hepatitis for ten years, a man in his 70s who did not like western medicine, took only Chinese herbal medicine as a treatment. However, on examination, it was found he had a two-centimeter tumor in his liver, and his doctor recommended surgery, saying, "If we get it out now, we have a chance. But I can't guarantee anything if we leave it until later."

The patient refused to follow his advice. One of the reasons he refused to do so was because he knew about Pi-Water. He had been drinking energy water for two months before his liver cancer was detected.

When the cancer was found, he began taking UFO along with the energy water. On so doing, amazingly, only two days later, the pain and the nausea disappeared. He then continued to take UFO along with energy water without taking any other kind of medicine whatsoever.

Four months after his cancer had been detected, with Pi-Water as his only medication, he began to convalesce, and he returned to the hospital for another examination. His tumor was found to have shrunk to one centimeter, and moreover there was hardly any detectable difference between his cells and ordinary cells. It seems that all the doctor could do was to look astonished.

Certainly, cancer progresses much more slowly in older people than in younger people. Also, there are occasionally cases of a cancer going into remission naturally without any kind of treatment. A doctor might be inclined to think along these lines. But the fact is, as I have described, that the only thing that this man did for his health after being diagnosed with cancer was to take Pi-Water, and nothing else.

Next, let's look at a clinical example of a case of liver cancer in which the sufferer has taken BES. For three years after being diagnosed with liver cancer, a 61-year-old man took anti-cancer drugs. He then began to take BES at the normal dosage for such cases of 54 drops per day.

Along with this, he took Chinese herbal medicine. Two months later, his symptoms had shown a remarkable improvement, so his liver was tested. The results are given below. The figures in parentheses give the values for just before beginning BES:

GOT: 48 (53)
GPT: 28 (65)
gamma-GTP: 82.4 (192.4)

The normal value for GOT is between 8 and 40. A value of over 50 is considered to be abnormal. At this point, a more thorough investigation would be considered appropriate. In this case, his value was not within the normal range, but he was below the 50 mark and getting closer to the normal range.

The normal value for GPT is between 5 and 40, so he was within the normal range. The normal value for a male for gamma-GTP is below 60. He was still above this normal value, but if we compare it to the former value, it had decreased markedly. I believe that this shows the effect of Pi-Water.

Next is a personal experience of liver cancer in a 63-year-old woman:

"I had a blood test and was told they suspected cirrhosis and liver cancer. I used to get tired very easily, and I was already aware of a heavy dull pain in my liver. I had been taking some Chinese herbal medicine and Vitamin C on a friend's recommendation, but it didn't seem to make any real difference. At this point, they found I had a polyp in my colon.

"An acquaintance of mine was worried about me and brought me some UFO. Starting as soon as I got up in the morning, at 10 am, noon, 3 pm, and 5 pm, five times a day, I put it in 200 cc of energy water and drank it. About a week later I could actually start to see a change. That special feature of cirrhosis, that reddening of the palms, began to fade, and I no longer noticed that dull heavy pain in my liver.

"One month after beginning UFO, I went to the hospital to get a blood test, and my GOT was 20, and my GPT was 10. Both had gone down. I wasn't taking any medicine, so I'm convinced this was all due to the effect of UFO. I am hopeful about the future, and intend to keep on drinking it until my values return to normal."

## PERSONAL EXPERIENCE AND CLINICAL EXAMPLES OF OTHER TYPES OF CANCER

There are also a number of clinical examples of surprising recovery in other forms of cancer and personal reports of major improvements in symptoms. I have decided to select a few of these to introduce to you.

First, please read through this personal account of the treatment a certain S.N. received for her uterine cancer.

On the 29th of July, 1991, my life took on a daily suffering I cannot fully relate even now. I had always been healthy and had never considered myself as a sick kind of person. However, in January of 1991, I had a sudden abnormal hemorrhage. This continued for some time, but I couldn't get used to the idea of going to a hospital. It was at this point that a friend pushed me to go. So, still feeling down, some six months now since my first hemorrhage, I went the local gynecological hospital for a checkup. They referred me to a doctor at a famous university hospital in my town. There they gave me various pathological tests, and the result was that I was diagnosed as early stage cancer. They said that surgery could be done about two to three months later.

I talked to my friends about my problem again, and this time they recommended I visit a local famous cancer specialist hospital. My doctor gave me a referral, and I went along. They gave me a blood test and found that I had malignant uterine cancer. It was fairly advanced, and moreover it was diagnosed as a gland cancer, which is very difficult to treat. I was admitted the same day and was told that I had to have surgery at the earliest opportunity. That was beginning of my terrible struggle against cancer, the worry and pain of which other people will never be able to understand.

In the hospital, I was transferred from the doctor who had originally tested me to a female doctor. She told me that there was a 70 percent chance that surgery would be out of the question in my case. So I took another batch of tests, and the result was that they would open me up, but couldn't say how it would turn out after that. On the 15th of August, 1991, they cut me open.

They found that, miraculously, my cancer hadn't yet spread. However, they were worried that they might have to remove my uterus or that it might metastasize sometime in the future, so they removed my ovaries completely. I was told I would be taking a five-session course of anticancer drugs (ten days between each session) and receiving 25 to 30 sessions of radiotherapy. Although I refused both anticancer drugs and radiotherapy, I was in hospital and in no position to really refuse a doctor's advice. Thus it was that I began to receive anticancer drugs and radiotherapy.

Later on, about one week following surgery, my friend brought me some high-energy Pi-Water and told me about it so I gave it a try. When I did, I found that it was different from other stuff I had drunk: I found it went down easily, and I could drink it naturally. Soon, I had a bottle of mineral water by my bed, and I would put some high-energy Pi-Water in it every day and drink two to three liters. The oral medicine the doctors prescribed I left completely untouched.

The result was that, even though I was on anticancer drugs, I only felt slightly sick, I was able to eat without throwing up, and my body showed absolutely no signs of swelling.

After surgery, I began radiotherapy, but on finishing my fifth session the doctors realized that it was having no effect on my illness, and they changed my treatment to anticancer drugs. As my white blood cells showed a slight reduction after my first dosage of the drug, they decided to wait and see before proceeding to the next. While I was waiting, I gathered reading material on anticancer drugs and did some study. This made me realize how scary they were. After my second session, I refused to take any more.

As a result, I noticed that the doctor's attitude toward me underwent a complete change, but, believing in the energy that high-energy Pi-Water has, I continued drinking it anyway. On leaving the hospital, the doctor told me that there was a good chance of the cancer's recurring after about one year, so I should come in for a regular checkup once every three months without fail. At that point, I thought I only had one or two more years to live.

After getting out of hospital, I got the Pi-Water purifier and from then on never failed to drink energy water and high-energy Pi-Water every day. In particular, I would mix high-energy Pi-Water with everything that I ate or drank. The result? Four years passed and I'm now in my fifth year following surgery, but no abnormalities have been found in my three-month checkups whatsoever, and I am able to lead a perfectly normal and healthy life. I love to travel, and I often go off traveling somewhere with a friend. I sometimes even drink alcohol and am able to enjoy each and every day.

Now I am bitter about my ovaries being completely removed, knowing that the cancer had not yet spread there at the time of my surgery and that they were healthy. At the same time, I feel somewhat suspicious of modern medicine. Now, each day I am able to lead a perfectly normal life thanks to high-energy Pi-Water. And for that I have to thank each and every day that dear friend who brought me high-energy Pi-Water at that time and who told me of its powers. (Quoted from the 1997 Spring edition of *Pi-Tech Forum*, published by the Association for Research and Propagation of Bio Energy Systems.)

The following are personal and clinical experiences of improvement in certain types of cancer:

- **Uterine cancer (67-year-old woman)**
  "Following surgery for uterine cancer, I developed ureterovaginal fistula, right hydronephrosis, and so on. I had a hard time of it. Moreover, my entire leg was swollen from the thigh to the instep. I went to the hospital, and they diagnosed blockage of the veins. Luckily, I was in time to prevent any tearing of the veins but was told that massage was out of the question as it might release a blood clot. All I could do was to take Chinese herbal medicine and wait for a natural recovery.

  "After leaving the hospital, someone recommended energy water, so I started drinking it. I hadn't drunk plain water since I was young, and I was uneasy about whether I would be able to drink large amounts of it. However, I found I had no problem getting energy water down. When I started drinking it, the first thing that happened was that the sensation of having urine left over disappeared. Then the swelling in my legs went away, and I started to feel much better as a whole."

- **Laryngeal cancer (48-year-old man)**
  In this case, the man's voice became rather husky, so he went to the hospital for a checkup. They found he had a laryngeal tumor. The tumor had spread in a wide area around his right-side vocal cords, and he could hardly speak. He began by taking 15 drops of BES per day, and from the fifth day on his voice became a little better.

  At that point he began radiotherapy (five times per week) and a course of anticancer drugs (twice a week). This lasted two months. During that time, he continued to take BES just as before. The usual side effects of the treatment failed to materialize, and he was able to continue more or less as normal.

  He later underwent the same kind of treatment three more times, and, as a result, the tumor disappeared. He then continued with the BES at a reduced dosage of ten drops per day. This could be interpreted as an example of radiotherapy and anticancer drugs working to beat cancer. However, there is no doubt that BES worked to alleviate the usual side effects of such treatment and to enhance its healing effect.

- **Benign brain tumor (39-year-old man)**
  He had a CT scan and was discovered to have a brain tumor. It was benign, but it was decided that surgery was impossible, given its location and size. He took 54 drops of BES per day in conjunction with Chinese herbal medicine (Ninjin-youei-to). Six months after beginning BES, he was examined again at the hospital. The results showed that his tumor had shrunk.

- **Leukemia (45-year-old woman)**
  This patient was a case of acute bone marrow leukemia. She was given BES along with Chinese herbal medicine (Rikkunshi-to) for approximately one year. At her 12-month checkup, it was found that, compared to her six-month checkup, her headaches, stiffness of the shoulders, back pain, constipation, halitosis, and so on had all disappeared. Her white blood corpuscle count had also risen.

- **Cancer of the urethra (68-year-old man)**
  "I was told I had cancer of the urethra in 1991. I began taking UFO some three months following surgery. The side effects from treatment with anticancer drugs are severe, but in my case I didn't feel so bad. I believe I have UFO to thank for that.

  "The first time I took anticancer drugs, I didn't know anything about UFO, but my white blood cell count had fallen to 1,000, and it was quite some time before that value was to rise again. By the time I did the second round of anticancer drugs, I was already drinking one bottle of UFO (10 milliliters). This time, my white blood cell count had only fallen as far as 3,800, and four days later it was up to 4,600."

- **Prostate cancer (76-year-old man)**
  "I was diagnosed with prostate cancer. I was told it was spreading to my stomach. I had absolutely no appetite, and if I pushed myself to eat, I would feel like throwing up. I was completely exhausted and could only lie down all the time. But when I started to drink UFO, my appetite returned, and on good days I could even eat three square meals again. Moreover, I could go for a stroll, and even felt like doing things like puttering around in the garden.

  "Before, I had had surgery on my kidneys so I would be able to urinate with the aid of a tube. But later they took out the tube, and I was able to urinate without it. I expect that if I go on drinking high-energy Pi-Water, I will eventually be able to completely root out the cancer lurking inside my body."

***Side effects of anticancer drugs and cancer pain disappear***

Generally, a course of anticancer drugs will be accompanied by a number of violent side effects such as vomiting and loss of hair. In a clinical test carried out at a hospital in Hungary, patients were given 25 drops of high-energy Pi-Water, UFO per day. With this treatment, these side effects disappeared. Moreover, end stage cancer usually brings violent pain, but this too was alleviated by the same dosage of UFO, and some cases were reported where morphine was unnecessary.

### IMPROVEMENT IN DAMAGE TO BLOOD VESSELS OF BRAIN

Damage to the blood vessels of the brain ranks as one of the three major causes of death among Japanese along with cancer and other adult diseases. In this area, too, the benefits that Pi-Water offers deserve attention.

With damage to the blood vessels of the brain, we have disorders like brain hemorrhages, infarctions, and so on—all problems arising from blockage of the blood flow through the brain. Often, such problems are accompanied by language impairment and paralysis. It is one of the biggest fears of people in their middle age and older.

I will now go on to give you three examples, all of which concern people with brain blood vessel related diseases that have left them with severe impairment of normal function. The results of using Pi-Water in all these cases deserve attention. The following is a report by Dr. Masatoshi Maeda of the Yamaguchi Rehabilitation Hospital:

> Mr. X (58 years old at the time) had been managing a company. However, he developed a brain infarction that affected the brainstem area, so he became quadriplegic (unable to use his hands and legs) and suffered from language impairment (aphasia), all serious aftereffects of his condition.

After receiving treatment at a large hospital, he transferred to us (Yamaguchi Rehabilitation Hospital). Here, he tried rehabilitation, but there were no signs of any improvement, and he was to be bedridden for another two years. His mental capacity was unimpaired, but he had no way to communicate. The only thing he could do was to focus his eyes on certain letters written on a board; this way, people could sometimes read what he was trying to say.

Mr. Y (63 years old at the time) had suffered partial paralysis to the right side of his body after a brain infarction at the age of 52. He had managed to continue with his life after that until he was struck again with another infarction, leaving him with paralysis to the left side, too, along with language impairment. In effect, this left him a quadriplegic, the same as Mr. X. What was particularly fortunate for this case was that his original right side paralysis had not been so severe, and he had eventually even been able to write with his right hand.

Rehabilitation and language therapy failed to improve his condition. He was judged to be beyond recovery by a team of specialists (various doctors, physiotherapists, and language therapists who decide the viability of each case). In other words, he was considered beyond the help of modern medicine.

Mr. Z (62 years old ) had suffered a brain infarction and was paralyzed on his left side and unable to communicate verbally. Moreover, the damage had extended to various vital areas of the brain, and his comprehension, memory, volition, and emotional state were all impaired. He was totally uninterested in anything and couldn't read even the simplest words.

All three patients were among some of the most serious at our hospital, and we decided to try Pi-Water with all three. First, we applied ointment to the head, then hair cream on top of that. We also applied oil to those areas of the body that were paralyzed. We continued this treatment once a day.

Next, we had them drink five drops of BES per day (morning, noon, and evening at two, one, and two drops, respectively) in 200 cc of energy water. It was recommended that they drink as much energy water as they could. We then waited and watched. A summary of the results is given as follows:

**Mr. X (treatment began on January 11)**
February 10: making noises and laughing while watching TV
February 13: "Seems much livelier than before" (comment from wife)
March 3: Manages to reply with a, "Um"
March 11: Manages to hum for first time
March 15: Sings a children's ditty
March 19: Says "Good morning"

**Mr. Y (treatment began on January 13)**
February 10: "His expression seems more normal; his eyes seem to sparkle" (comments by wife)
February 24: Laughs. Is able to say, "Good morning" quite clearly
April 13: Although they are unclear, he is able to tell jokes

**Mr. Z (treatment began on January 13)**
March 9: Facial expression clear
March 16: Able to say, "Yes" and "That's OK." Is able to laugh well
March 23: Is able to talk in a loud voice and laugh
March 30: "Has started watching golf on TV where he showed no interest before" (comment by wife)
April 12: "Shows his feelings in his facial expressions" (comment by wife)

Whether these effects are due to Pi-Water, or whether they are due to something else, we don't yet know. Dr. Maeda believes that, "Pi-Water may be a type of energy (chi) emanating water."

### Pi-Water acts to tune the body

We have now mentioned the word *chi* (that which is found in Chinese Tai Chi). Therefore, let us look more closely at the secret of the healing effect of Pi-Water in relation to this. I will now go on to describe what I think after confirming the effect of Pi-Water on various types of cancer and adult diseases, those that I have discussed above, with my own eyes.

One particular feature of Pi-Water is its small clusters. This means that the molecules of the water are diffused in small groups throughout the water, making it easier for the water to be absorbed thoroughly by any other substance.

Therefore, if you compare a cucumber raised in Pi-Water with one raised in ordinary water, you find that the former is always as fresh as if it had just been bought from the shop, even when the latter has already shriveled.

This is because, with Pi-Water, the water molecules have been able to thoroughly permeate the cucumber. If the water molecules have been able to thoroughly permeate the cucumber, this means that the cells of the plant will be at their most healthy. To put it another way, this means that the energy level of the plant will be heightened.

Looked at from the macroscopic perspective, I believe that all energy can be seen as cosmic energy that has assumed a different form. It will differ according to its wave. What is life? It is the result of a conversion of the energies of air, water, earth, and light. Those energies are taken into the body, broken down, and re-assembled. Thus, we convert them into an energy that can be used in our own particular living body. Our bodies exist under conditions of normal temperature and pressure. Therefore, chemical reactions far exceeding those in any giant chemical factory are only made possible within us by virtue of this incredibly fine tuning mechanism we all possess.

However, there is something in our lifestyle that can impede that mechanism. This life-supporting mechanism with which we are all blessed is sometimes not allowed to do its work. Thus, we become unable to properly assimilate the energy we need. The biggest cause of this breakdown in this mechanism is the activated oxygen I refer to in Chapter Two.

If activated oxygen posed no threat to our bodies, we would be able to live free from illness, and the process of aging would be limited to its natural speed of development; we would certainly be able to live out the natural life span given us by the cosmos. It is thought that those people who live beyond 100 years in good health and vigor have found some way to attain that state.

Until now, we have had no idea what that might be. Even now, we can't say that we completely understand. However, it is certain that Pi-Water acts as some kind of energy converter. If that were not the case, there is no way that life would be enhanced by water, a conductor that contains no special nutrients.

This brings us to the its connection with the chi we saw mentioned in chi water just now. It would seem that chi energy definitely exists. So when can we witness the manifestation of chi? It is said that, under certain specific conditions, it will show itself when it directly comes up against another energy force.

For example, there is a patient and a chi practitioner, and the patient really wants to be cured. Therefore, he really trusts the chi practitioner. The practitioner, too, really wants to help the patient, so he concentrates that desire intensely. Then, we see the coming together head-on of the wills of the patient and the practitioner, two people who are in a diametrically opposed state. It is at this point that chi power is able to flow.

This is something that transcends the gap between physical entities and human beings. We have a force we call magnetism. When the magnetism from opposite poles meets, a negative magnetic field is produced. At this point, human will can affect physical substances, and we are able to absorb the energy of those substances as convertible energy. It is possible to think of ferric ferrous salts that produce Pi-Water as having the same ability as such negative magnetism.

It is Pi-Water that gives us this special ability by utilizing the particular powers of ferric ferrous salts. And I believe that it is by taking in Pi-Water that we are able to absorb the various kinds of good cosmic energy, the energy we need.

Modern medicine has classified illness into so many different names and categories that the doctors themselves can't even remember them all. But all these diseases have but one root cause. And I understand the root cause to be a deficiency of bio-energy. If this were not the case, it would be unthinkable for Pi-Water to be so effective in bringing about an improvement in so many different diseases.

One generally finds that in modern medicine, if you say something is effective for all illnesses, everyone takes it to mean that it has only a slight effect or that it doesn't really work at all. Cold medicine will cure athlete's foot. Medicine for high blood pressure will relieve itchiness. Common sense tells us that this could not be so. But that is only because we take each and every sickness to be something different.

If we look at sickness from the macroscopic perspective (as an abnormality in the living organism), then a cold, athlete's foot, high blood pressure, even dermatitis may be regarded as one and the same: an abnormality in the living organism. Pi-Water doesn't have the ability to attack each and every illness specifically. But I believe it can effect an improvement by tackling the main problem, by acting on the lack of bio-energy that lies at the root of all illness.

# CHAPTER FOUR

❁ ❁ ❁

## IF CELLS ARE REJUVENATED, THE BODY CAN BE HEALED

## MORE CASES OF REAL ROOT CURE FOR PEOPLE WITH PREDISPOSITION TOWARD ATOPIC ECZEMA

In the previous chapter I explained how useful Pi-Water was in treating cancer and other adult lifestyle related diseases. However, in this chapter, I would like to mention the possibilities of Pi-Water in relation to other illnesses and physical problems, as well as its role in preserving beauty and youth.

First, let's look at atopic dermatitis. This has shown a remarkable increase in recent years. There are many facets of this illness that are as yet medically unexplained. Nor has any real method of treatment been established. It is a difficult disease to live with, and the number of both adults and children afflicted with this disease continues to grow. So what effect has Pi-Water had on this particular disease?

Let me cite some personal experiences of improvement of atopic eczema:

- **Atopic eczema #1 (11-year-old boy)**

  "I first got atopic eczema three months after I was born. All around my neck, layers of hardened skin formed like the scales of some snake. It would itch, and unconsciously I would scratch it open during the night. In the morning the sheets would be covered in blood. The whole of my upper body was covered in these scales, and my skin would just crumble and fall away like dandruff. So they tried steroids."

  This boy had severe symptoms and was in great distress. On trying Pi-Water, the following change occurred. This is how his mother describes it:

  "At first, the eczema got much worse. I was really shocked. I thought I'd made a big mistake. But considering how bad the eczema had become, he was suffering much less than before from the itching. So I decided to wait and see. To look at him, his symptoms continued to worsen for some time after that. But, as soon as he really made up his mind to stop taking other medicine altogether, things started to change. From then on, things really started to improve. Now, it's almost completely cleared up."

Even when he went to school, the boy would take a thermos of water with him. Every day he would drink 1.5 liters of energy water. Moreover, his food was soaked in energy water before it was cooked. He would even spray his bread with it before toasting it. Nothing was left to chance.

I can imagine how hard it must have been for his mother, but her efforts paid off. Now, the only thing he gets is a little sweat rash from time to time. Apparently his skin is now soft and sleek.

- **Atopic Eczema #2 (26-year-old woman)**

"Whenever summer comes around, I get a rash. It's not just itchy; it's not nice to look at either. In the season where you would usually show your skin, I couldn't really even date anybody. A friend recommended energy water, so I started drinking it. The next summer, I only got a light case, and the itchiness was much better. My skin now looks lustrous and healthy."

This lady is now a big fan of energy water. She uses it in every aspect of her life: as water for flowers, to cook rice and other foods, and so on. She says she feels much better now. A single girl, she maintains that the first thing that's going into her trousseau will be a Pi-Water Purifier.

- **Atopic Eczema #3 (25-year-old woman)**

"I've had atopic eczema since I was small, and I have nothing but horrible memories of it. I sort of half gave up, thinking it was my natural disposition, but then I heard about Pi-Water. I thought, 'Just maybe…' With this glimmer of hope, I decided to try putting five pails of energy water into my bath every day. And what do you think happened? The dryness gradually disappeared, and my skin became lovely and sleek again."

- **Atopic Eczema #4 (22-year-old man)**

Let us look at another example of a man suffering from a rather severe case of atopic eczema. This man had a rash on many areas of his body. In particular, this was accompanied by a terrible itchiness in his shoulders, neck, and around his joints. At a touch, his skin would flake and fall away like dandruff.

"I tried a number of different treatments, but nothing seemed to really work. I sort of gave up. It was around then that someone introduced me to UFO. I was desperate and ready to try anything, so I began to take it along with energy water. The itchiness gradually subsided. I went on taking it, and the skin on my back began to get better. I began to hope that this might be able to really cure me."

- **Atopic Eczema #5 (54-year-old man)**
  "I have had atopic eczema for 17 years and have covered myself with steroids. As a result, my face has turned a dark-brown color, and you can tell I have eczema at a glance. Even with the steroids, there was no way I could even play golf in the summer because the itching was so bad.

  "Then I came across Pi-Water. I started using PAISEIREI, energy water, and Pi-Time (Pi-solvent for the bath). I was instructed to drink PAISEIREI at a rate of ten drops at a time, three times a day, but I wanted to get cured quickly, so I took double the dose, that is 20 drops each time, three times a day (I stopped taking the steroids). I had been warned beforehand about the way a good reaction might appear. Three or four days after I started treatment, my rash just exploded, and my face was all swollen up. However, that peaked on the tenth day, and after that it quickly started to clear up. Forty days later it was completely gone. Since then, I haven't touched steroids even once. I can drink alcohol and eat grilled meat now, no problem. Pi-Water is really amazing."

As in the above example, drinking high-energy Pi-Water can also sometimes cause a strong reaction. When the reaction period ends, the eczema will be cured, too. But if the reaction is so severe as to be unbearable, then decrease the dosage by half.

With children and females, you should start with two to three drops, three times per day, increasing the dose gradually as you go. If a child suffers from itchiness, rub a drop of high-energy Pi-Water onto the affected spot. It will sting for just a second, but it will get rid of the itchiness.

### WORKING FROM THE INSIDE TO REJUVENATE CELLS AND CREATE BEAUTIFUL SKIN

It is said that the foundation of all beauty lies within (inner cosmetics). In other words, unless you start from the inside in creating beauty, however much you may work on the outside, the end result will only be superficial. However, these days, inner beauty is difficult to achieve. We must contend with environmental pollution and food tainted with chemicals everywhere. Everybody is stressed out. There is absolutely no shortage of things to prevent us from achieving inner beauty. The deterioration in the quality of our drinking water is serious. Even the smelly water produced by chlorination would be better than the water that is used in many condominiums. They often draw water directly from a storage tank and use it as drinking water.

If such water is not properly handled, it is not just unpleasant to taste, it is bacterially, minerally, and chemically polluted. There is the danger of damage to our health by double or even triple pollution here.

Here are some personal experiences desribing skin care:

- **Creating beautiful skin #1 (28-year-old woman)**

  "I had been aware of the danger from and unpleasantness of tap water for some time. When I found out about the Pi-Water Purifier, I did not hesitate in getting one immediately. On first drinking energy water, I felt like it was really permeating my body. I had no idea water could taste so nice. I was really impressed. It completely changed my feelings about water."

  In this case, in addition to completely switching over to Pi-Water from ordinary water, she also made a point of always using Pi-Water whenever water was needed with vegetables, fruit, meat, or even fish. Moreover, she would put two or three pails of Pi-Water into her bath when she got it ready.

Before even one month had passed after getting the Pi-Water Purifier, she was able to confirm for herself the miraculous effect of Pi-Water in creating beautiful skin. In the morning, when she washed her face, her skin felt completely different to the touch. It was soft and lustrous. It had apparently never felt like that before.

On taking a bath, she would look at herself in the mirror. Again, her skin had taken on a new sleek appearance. It seems she even forgot all about the various toilet waters and body lotions she had considered so important.

Even her husband, who had been skeptical at first, found that the headaches that had plagued him just disappeared after using Pi-Water. He couldn't believe it. When his hangovers disappeared, too, he was overjoyed. In other words, they are both much healthier and happier now.

- **Creating beautiful skin #2 (33-year-old woman)**
  "My eldest son had a problem with a rash caused by oversecretion of his sebaceous glands all over his face from when he was born. When my second son was born, I got a Pi-Water Purifier so I could bath him in energy water. Thanks to that, he has spotless skin. Didn't even have any problem with diaper rash. Nothing gave me greater pleasure than always being able to see him sleeping soundly with such a fresh face. My eldest son's skin also got better and better."

Everybody wants to be healthy and beautiful. Therefore, people want to rejuvenate their cells. One cause of aging skin is the influence of activated oxygen and ultraviolet light. However, those factors aside, the primary cause is thought to lie in an energy deficiency in the epidermal (skin) cells. So why is there this energy deficiency in the epidermal cells?

No matter how healthy you might be, with the passing of each day the aging process will continue. Epidermal cells have a life span: when they have divided a certain number of times, that division comes to a halt, and they wither and die. However, this should not be misunderstood as meaning that these cells have the same life span as we do, that is to say, somewhere in the region of 80 to 100 years.

It is far longer; at the most conservative estimate, a cell's life span is considered to be about five times that taken to reach the point of full growth (the point of full mental and physical maturity) of a human being. If we calculate that it would take 25 years for a human being to reach full maturity, then that would bring a cell's life span to 125 years. Therefore, a period of 40 or 50 years is too soon for skin to deteriorate. Our lifestyle would appear to be an important factor in determining this figure.

It is said that, in particular, we are capable of maintaining healthy skin much longer than we can maintain our internal organs. According to one world authority on skin medicine, Dr. Kramen, if we look after our skin, we should be able to easily preserve it in the condition it is in our 30s and 40s well into our 60s.

The skin care that we are talking of here refers to both external care and care from the inside. We cannot look after our internal organs by external measures, but with skin we can. This can be counted as a primary reason why we are able to preserve our skin longer than we can our organs.

If we ask which is most important, external or internal care, then the answer is internal, absolutely. The biggest prerequisite in preserving youthful skin is delivering nutrition to our skin and getting rid of decaying waste products as quickly as possible.

Once that is taken care of, if we can apply external care as well, then our skin will remain fresh much longer because of the compound effect. Pi-Water has proved to be effective for external use, but it also has enormous power to rejuvenate cells from within. Therefore, just drinking Pi-Water will change skin so much we won't recognize it. There have been many reports of people experiencing a complete rejuvenation of their skin, with their spots and freckles disappearing, after using cosmetics that incorporate Pi-Water. Skin can be seen, so results are easy to see, but if you drink Pi-Water, an even greater effect is taking place on the inside, too. From the viewpoint of cell rejuvenation, it would be ideal to use the Pi-Water system both externally and internally.

### DRINKING PI-WATER EVERY DAY WILL RELIEVE STUBBORN CONSTIPATION

Nobody allows diarrhea to continue indefinitely, but there would appear to be many who don't take constipation seriously enough. Some even boast how long they've gone without passing stool. You hear things like, "Me? Oh, about a week," and somebody else replying, "Really? It's been ten days or more for me!"

Please think of constipation as being the greatest enemy of health and youthfulness. If constipation continues over a number of years, it will result in a number of beauty problems such as dry skin, skin eruptions, allergic rashes, blotchiness, and freckles. It will also lead to a number of health problems such as headaches, dizziness, insomnia, and stiff shoulders.

However, these are discomforts; they are not illnesses. Therefore, some people just ignore them. The body then grows accustomed to being in that state. The more you get used to it, the less you notice it. This, though, is a dangerous situation.

Without realizing it, in so doing, you pave the way for various serious adult lifestyle diseases to take hold such as hardening of the arteries, strokes, heart disease, liver disease, kidney disease, and cancer of the colon. And, on top of that, you hasten the process of aging. Moreover, constipation will cause poisonous gases to be produced inside the body. These will be carried around the body via the blood, so they will even exert their bad effect on the cells of the brain.

Again, long-term constipation has even been cited as the cause of dementia. Therefore, it is important to recognize constipation as an illness that must by treated quickly and to do something about it. So what effect does Pi-Water have on constipation? Let's read about personal experiences using Pi-Water to treat constipation:

- **Constipation #1 (22-year-old woman)**
  "I've always had a tendency toward constipation, so passing stool has always been a painful chore for me. On top of that, sometimes I found I had bloody stool. When I had long bouts of constipation, I would feel numb all over and just didn't seem to be myself. Sometimes, I just couldn't stand the thought of the pain and would hold it in, even though I wanted to go to the lavatory. But I didn't want to take medicine, as I was afraid I would come to depend on it."

  This is a typical case of constipation. One day, she heard about high-energy Pi-Water from a friend who said that, "Some people have had their constipation cured by it." So she began to drink it. From about the second month, she saw a real improvement: her bloody stool ceased, and after six months she began to experience regular bowel movements.

- **Constipation #2 (37-year-old woman)**
  "For a long time, I suffered from stubborn constipation. At the same time, I would get stomach pain and stiff shoulders. I tried various drugs, but to no effect whatsoever. Just as I was about to give up, someone recommended energy water to me. I was skeptical at first as all it does is purify ordinary tap water, but one month after I started drinking it, I started to feel better. Now, I don't have to worry about constipation at all."

- **Constipation #3 (32-year-old woman)**
  "I was pregnant at the time. I started getting constipated around the time my morning sickness started. The hospital

told me I had anemia brought on by a deficiency in iron. When I started to take the medicine they gave me for it, I began getting bouts of both constipation and diarrhea as side effects. It was really uncomfortable. It was around then that I found out about energy water. I began taking it, believing in what was said about amniotic fluids' becoming purer. It tasted really good, so it was easy to drink. So good that I really got into drinking it, and before I knew it, my bowel movements had become regular."

- **Constipation #4 (53-year-old woman)**
  "I've suffered from chronic constipation ever since I was a child. So I had always relied on medicine for which I had to fork over a small fortune. Then, one day, I made up my mind to switch completely to energy water and give it a go. I would drink two or three cups the moment I got up. Later, whenever I had the chance, whether before or after meals, I would drink more. Thanks to that, my constipation really cleared up. I was so surprised! My stool even smelled better and looked a healthier color."

- **Constipation #5 (51-year-old man)**
  "I have always been interested in water, and when I found out about energy water, I immediately got some in. However, my family thought it was crazy. I thought that, rather than talking about it, I should first give it a try. So, I would drink two large glasses every morning and one every night. From about the third week, my stool, which had smelled pretty bad before, began to lose its odor. I was passing more than before and more regularly. Now, my wife even takes some energy water to work with her in a thermos, saying, 'I can't drink tap water at work any more.'"

In order to fight constipation, it is considered important to eat food high in fiber and to drink plenty of liquids. Certainly, it would seem that people prone to constipation tend not to take enough fluids. However, to think that if it's water then it must be okay is a mistake: sadly, the tap water available nowadays is well below the standard we need if it is to be drunk as it is. Even if we use the mineral water you can get in the shops just for drinking, it soon becomes very expensive.

I believe that the best thing, both in terms of the amount you can consume and economics, is to make energy water available to your whole family. Furthermore, as happened with the wife mentioned in example #5, it is perfectly all right to take energy water to work with you in a thermos. But it is more convenient to use high energy Pi-Water if you are going to be walking around with it.

Whenever I go out somewhere, I always carry one or two bottles of UFO in my pocket. If you have some with you, you can quickly change whatever water is available into energy water by adding a couple of drops. One good idea is to use energy water at home and carry UFO whenever you go out.

### ENERGY WATER WILL ELIMINATE FATIGUE

Fatigue itself is not an illness so it is not something to worry about as such. However, there are probably many people who have real problems with fatigue. The fact is, however much you may say that it is not an illness, if your body feels fatigued, you can't really tackle anything with a positive attitude.

If you can't get enthusiastic about either your work or your play, then your life will lose all its vitality. It is by no means rare to find people who, not realizing that they are suffering from constant fatigue, go about their lives in a depression thinking that life is just boring.

It is quite common to find people who, on starting to drink Pi-Water, make comments like "I feel much better within myself," and "I feel much more enthusiastic about doing things." They find themselves more positive than before. This is evidence that they themselves are feeling physically better. It could probably be said that a large part of people's worries could be attributed to being physically out of condition.

A few personal experiences can illustrate Pi-Water's effect:

- **Recovery from fatigue #1 (54-year-old woman)**
"I moved to a new apartment, and the biggest problem I had was with the poor quality of the water. If that had been all, then it wouldn't have been so bad. But I often suffered physical debilitation. I realized it was because the water didn't agree with me, but there was nothing I could do. One time when I was particularly worried about this and that, I found out about energy water."

She discussed the matter with her husband, but he quickly opposed the idea, saying it was too expensive. However, insisting that nothing can replace good health, she talked him into buying it. After installing the Pi-Water Purifier, they found that their previously undrinkable water had begun to taste good. It seems that, too, soon after they began drinking it, their chronic physical debility disappeared.

It is said that diet is important in maintaining health, but water is just as important, too. If the quality of the water you drink everyday is poor, then the effect of any nutrition you absorb will be halved, however much attention you pay to your diet. It is very likely that her physical debility was attributable to the poor quality of the water in her apartment.

Even more sensitive to water quality than humans are plants. Plants are the same as people in that they require water to live. There are examples of plants also undergoing the same kind of change the above woman experienced on installing the Pi-Water Purifier. Plants that had somehow seemed sick really revived on being given Pi-Water. The color and appearance of the leaves became much better. The plants, too, had been tired because of the quality of city water.

- **Recovery from fatigue #2 (30-year-old woman)**
"I used to get really stiff shoulders all the time, and I couldn't sleep at night. The whole area around my shoulders was as

stiff as a board, and sometimes I would even feel sick or get headaches with it. I tried seeing doctors, but they couldn't find the cause. I was completely at a loss as to what to do. By chance, I found out about Pi-Water. If it would help even a little, I was ready to try anything, so I installed the purifier. Around two months or more after I started drinking it, my shoulder muscles began to untangle and feel lighter. Now I don't suffer from stiff shoulders at all and can sleep soundly at nights. I can hardly believe that just drinking water can make such a difference."

- **Recovery from fatigue #3 (58-year-old woman)**
  "I used to get stiff shoulders and chronic fatigue. One time, when I was having chi treatment and acupuncture/moxibustion, somebody told me about Pi-Water. I got the water purifier and soon made it a habit to drink two cups everyday on getting up and going to bed. After that, I would drink it whenever I had the chance. It started to take effect after the first week. Every morning, about one hour after drinking it, I would pass stool and produce double the amount of urine I had been able to before."

  In her case, she says that around four months later she no longer felt fatigued and could work each day full of energy. And she wouldn't feel tired the next day either. Moreover, it seems that her sense of dullness on getting up in the morning and stiff shoulders had disappeared before she knew it.

  This is a typical case of what happens when beginning to drink Pi-Water. It takes about three to four months to completely change the water content of your body. It will vary a little depending on the individual. However, even people who have been drinking poor quality water will be able to effect such a change within this time period. Every blood cell in their body will be thoroughly permeated with moisture rejuvenated by Pi-Water. When this happens, all sorts of physical problems will disappear as a result of a heightened immune system and rejuvenated powers of self-recovery.

- **Recovery from Fatigue #4 (51-year-old woman)**
  "Before I drank energy water I always somehow felt out of condition and would always catch colds all year round. The area around my mouth was always dry, and the skin around the corners of my mouth would often crack. After starting to drink energy water, I hardly caught colds at all, and when I did they were only light ones. I used to really love it when people would say, 'You look really healthy these days.' I now look forward to drinking water, something I used to think was just a chore."

  This person had probably been chronically short of water before. When the amount of water absorbed into the body is low, the blood and other bodily fluids thicken and the metabolism suffers. It goes without saying that the quality of the water is important, but the amount is important, too. Furthermore, colds can be regarded as an indicator of the body's health as a whole. If someone is always catching colds, it is evident that he or she has some physical conditioning or lifestyle problem. You shouldn't regard it as just a cold. You should try to avoid colds as an important part of maintaining your health and youth.

### WHILE MAKING YOUR BODY HEALTHY YOU CAN DIET

There is one clinical example of an extremely obese lady in her 20s who realized that she had really slimmed down after drinking five bottles of high-energy Pi-Water. In her case, she had originally started on the Pi-Water for a reason unrelated to her obesity so had not accompanied it with any diet regimen.

She had not been trying to lose weight, so why had she been able to slim down? What happened was that, in the process of her body becoming healthier by her drinking Pi-Water, the fat that had not been natural to her began to disappear in the course of treatment. Obesity is undesirable as it can lead to other adult diseases. However, to judge oneself to be obese based on relative height and weight without proper consideration of one's natural disposition is not so accurate. Regarding natural disposition to fat from birth, people can generally be categorized into three types:

1. The plump type. For their height and weight these people would probably be judged to be on the overweight side by the current index in use, but the fact is that that would be the right level of fat for that person.
2. Next is the normal type. Their weight could be calculated by subtracting 100 or 105 from any given height on the current index.
3. The third is the thin type. They will be four or five kilograms below the standard weight. These are the appropriate weights by type.

In other words, the weight appropriate to you will differ according to your natural type. It would seem that currently diets are oriented to making everybody into the thin type. However, it must be said that this is extremely dangerous.

It is clear that fashion models, for example, are much too thin. If you happen to be that type, then it's okay. But if someone who isn't naturally that type maintains such a physical condition and weight over many years, he or she can certainly expect to become sick or age quickly. Models are professionals and are probably aware of the risks. But for ordinary people to copy them can only be said to be foolish.

The fact is, as long as there is no special illness to intervene, if a person eats proper food, drinks good water and exercises appropriately, then he or she probably won't get fat.

These days, everybody seems to be on a diet. No method is left untried. However, nobody has managed to find a sure-fire way as yet.

On the other hand, there are many dangerous diet methods. So why do people seek some drastic diet plan? There are many overweight people, not just women but men, too. The best diet for them would be to adopt the right lifestyle rather than diet if they want to maintain the best weight for them.

There are many people who are very pleased, saying "I managed to diet!" after drinking Pi-Water and finding their weight reduced. However, this diet effect is no more than a result. People who were overweight will lose weight, but people who weren't will not. Therefore, it is a mistake to take Pi-Water for the purpose of dieting and say, "I've reduced!" Only people who were unnaturally fat will be sure to see a weight reduction by drinking Pi-Water. For example, the following personal experience of a 33-year-old woman will serve as an illustration:

> My younger sister put on weight after her pregnancy. All she could wear was a size 15. But two months after starting to drink energy water, she could fit into a size 11. In my case, I started drinking it because I had stiff shoulders and a low body temperature. However, three days later, my body temperature rose a degree, and my stiff shoulders disappeared after a month. Even though I was eating the same food as before, I lost several kilograms and my waist really trimmed down."

## WE NO LONGER NEED SPECIAL MEDICINE FOR ATHLETE'S FOOT

You often hear it said that if someone could come up with a perfect cure for the common cold or method for growing hair, they would be sure to get the Nobel Prize. There are some people who say the same about a cure for athlete's foot. That's how difficult it is to cure. However, there are many personal experiences of those who maintain that their athlete's foot has been cured by Pi-Water:

- **Cure for athlete's foot #1 (65-year-old woman)**
  "I had been plagued with stubborn athlete's foot for ten years. I had tried a number of different medicines, but nothing seemed to work. It was particularly bad whenever I wore nylon stockings. The white skin between my toes would all peel away. It would get so painful that it was difficult for me to walk.

"Then, one day, I heard from an acquaintance about this new water purifier that made good water that could rejuvenate blood cells. I already had a purifier that could dechlorinate water so I felt it was a bit of a waste, but...well, thinking it was for the health of the whole family, I got the Pi-Water purifier installed.

"I used to have a bad stomach. I would soon get carsick so riding in a taxi was out of the question. However, nowadays I can ride any amount of time, no problem. However, the thing that pleases me most is that my athlete's foot has completely disappeared. My feet are now beautifully clean."

- **Cure for athlete's foot #2 (48-year-old man)**
"I always used to be troubled with athlete's foot, and in the spring I would get hay fever. When I first got the Pi-Water Purifier, which a friend recommended to me, I didn't think for one minute that it would be effective against both. I drank it as ordinary drinking water, and it was very nice. I was quite satisfied with the fact it made coffee, soup, and rice taste so much better.

"At the beginning of spring, when my hay fever would always worsen, my friend told me to drink even more Pi-Water. So I gave it a try and managed to get through the season with an exceptionally light bout of hay fever. Feeling much better, I happily drank even more, and before I knew it, my athlete's foot completely disappeared."

In this case, it seems that, when he used medicine, the athlete's foot would temporarily subside. However, after a while it would return. Constant repetition of this cycle made him think it was a chronic problem, and he had half given up hope. I think that all athlete's foot sufferers feel pretty much the same way. But there are other examples, too, of people achieving an almost perfect cure by continuing to drink Pi-Water.

- **Cure of athlete's foot #3 (52-year-old man)**
"If I had to describe the changes for the better that occurred

in my body after I started to drink energy water, I would first mention how it cured my athlete's foot. Particularly in summer, I would get blisters that were unbearably itchy. But now I can hardly believe how completely they disappeared. After that, my bowels became much more regular, too. And I could also read and write without my glasses, something I could never do before because I'm farsighted and have astigmatism."

When someone says that athlete's foot has been cured when medicine, despite great strides, has only been able to come up with symptomatic treatments, experts will probably scoff. Even I don't know whether it has been perfectly cured from a medical point of view. However, it is certain that sufferers have experienced an improvement so great enough to say, "It's disappeared" or "It's cured."

Is it possible that such a thing could occur just because of water? I believe that this is perfectly possible. When you drink Pi-Water, first your metabolism will be revitalized. When each and every blood cell is rejuvenated, your immune system, too, will be revitalized. Your blood circulation will improve, and every kind of bodily function will work normally.

When your body is functioning normally, your ability to fight off ailments that are fundamentally incompatible with your body will heighten. When you drink plenty of Pi-Water, many diseases can be fended off. I believe that you create an unfriendly environment for the athlete's foot germ (a type of fungus known as *trichophyton*).

### DRINK MORE WITHOUT A HANGOVER

I always carry some UFO with me, and it's even proved useful when I go drinking. For example, if I add a few drops to whatever liquor or whisky being served, the liquor quickly goes up a notch in quality. I am very pleased about that.

What's more, even if I overdo it a little on the alcohol, it doesn't last over into the next day. I've no idea why, but I don't have any trouble with hangovers anymore. People who drink energy water often say this. I believe it is because the Pi-Water breaks heightens the body's ability to break down the alcohol.

It is even better if you add a few drops of high-energy Pi-Water to your alcohol. This is all you need as your defense against hangovers. You can use energy water, too. It is also good to add energy water to whisky or as hot water to be added to liquor. Here is a personal experience of a person who gave this a try:

- **Improvement in hangovers (29-year-old man)**
  "There were many times when I had to go drinking because of work. Sometimes, as many as three times a week I would wake up with a throbbing head from a hangover. I began to worry that if I continued like that I would end up getting some disease. However, I found out about energy water and quickly started drinking it. My hangovers completely disappeared.

  "I couldn't believe it, and I thought that I might be consuming less, so I began to keep a close watch on my drinking. However, it turned out I was still drinking the same amount. Therefore, to see whether energy water really was effective, I went to a local bar. There, I put some energy water on some cut-up apple and lettuce, and neither changed color as they usually do. Next, I tried adding it to some whisky. The taste was better than before, and I ended up drinking much more than usual."

This man's experiment was very interesting from the point of view of drinking alcohol. However, drinking more might become a bit of a problem. The Pi-Water showed its strength as an antioxident by preventing the apple and lettuce from changing color on being cut up. This effect demonstrates its ability to prevent the damage caused by activated oxygen, said to be the main cause of aging and adult diseases.

It would appear that the reason why people who drink energy water every day don't get hangovers is that it heightens the function of the liver and also strengthens the body's antioxidants.

In my experience though, it seems better not to use UFO with beer. It renders the beer too mild and causes it to lose its fresh taste.

### SELF-CLEANSING MECHANISM EXPELS TOXINS FROM BODY MORE EFFICIENTLY

Pi-Water has the power to help eliminate toxins that are usually difficult to expel from the body. Human beings maintain life by taking in air, water, and nutrition. However, things we don't need also enter the body. Moreover, the body itself creates unnecessary substances that must be expelled from the body.

Waste substances, unnecessary substances, and harmful material—all these must be expelled from the body. But when there is some problem with this elimination function or when the amount to be expelled is simply too much, then various kinds of damage can occur. For example, we have the kind of example that follows:

A 14-year-old boy suddenly found himself tiring easily and losing interest in everything. He began to put on weight at an alarming rate. He had been an extremely bright student and had been in the top of his class. However, after losing interest in everything, his grades went into an inevitable and relentless decline. Eventually, he ended up at the bottom of the class. As might be expected, his parents were worried about him and took him to a hospital where he was diagnosed with Wilson's disease. This disease is a type of malfunction of the body's metabolism that occurs when the body fails to expel copper.

If left untreated, there is the danger of damage to the body's motor ability and of developing mental problems. Unfortunately the cause is unknown, and, of course, there is no treatment for it. The only remedy is to take antitoxins. He took various medicines but to no effect. It was at this point that he found out about high-energy Pi-Water.

The family heard that Pi-Water worked as an antitoxin and biological purifier. They decided to give it a try. His body weight that had increased over a three-month period dropped 14 kilograms to its former level. At the same time, his physical strength and interest in activities returned. It would appear that this was attributable to the Pi-Water's stimulating his metabolism and expelling the copper that had built up in his system.

There was a case of a 52-year-old man with a seven-year history of dialysis. During the winter he had always worn stomach warmers and thick underwear. However, after drinking energy water he was able to make do with just a short-sleeved shirt. His white and red blood cell counts, which had been half that of ordinary people, returned to normal values.

So what does all this mean? It means that the body has been purified and the blood cells rejuvenated. When dust gets into a machine, it causes a disturbance in its ability to function. For example, when you clean something like the head of a tape recorder, the sound is so clear that it sounds completely different. The human body is the same. If you don't expel dead and other waste material from the body, it does not matter how many nutrients you may consume; they will not be absorbed into the body.

When you drink energy water, moisture is conveyed to every single cell in your body. Moreover, dead waste material will be carried away. As a result, tissue and cells will be rejuvenated. Therefore, the body will be able to function as it should.

One woman had surgery for a tumor in her uterus. On the third day after beginning to drink energy water, she noticed a purulent rash on her lower abdomen. She was surprised, but it was neither painful nor itchy. Realizing that this was a manifestation of Pi-Water's "improvement reaction" she let it go. Before long, it disappeared. After that, her health bloomed, and her skin became beautiful and lustrous. I believe that this was probably due to the toxins that had accumulated in her body being expelled.

It is impossible for modern human beings to avoid taking in poisons because of water pollution, atmospheric pollution, residual agricultural chemicals, food additives, medicines, and so on. The body should be capable of expelling foreign bodies. It does this by the mediation of water throughout the body.

However, the water we have now is deteriorating in quality, so rather than being purified, we end up being polluted by it. To put it graphically, it is as if we were trying to rinse laundry with dirty water. In this manner, no matter how many times we might go through the process, the objective of purification will not be reached. It is against this background that Pi-Water can provide us with clean water for the purification of our body.

### PI-WATER IS EFFECTIVE AGAINST PAIN ACCOMPANYING ILLNESS

Typical of those illnesses that are accompanied by pain is rheumatism. The cause of rheumatism is still not really known, but it is numbered among those illnesses related to collagen (connective tissue) problems. At the present time the primary remedy is to prescribe allopathic drugs to alleviate the pain. Unfortunately, these drugs are also accompanied by serious side effects.

What effect does Pi-Water have on those illnesses accompanied by pain? Let us look at the following personal experiences:

- **Rheumatism #1 (41-year-old woman)**
  "My right elbow and wrist are deformed, and I can't turn my palm upward. My right wrist is always painful. Lifting things and wringing out cloths were always extremely painful. Moreover, my fingers were all swollen. I knew that rheumatism was incurable and had given up hope, but I found out about high-energy Pi-Water and heard various explanations about it. Not holding out much hope, I started to drink one drop of Pi-Water every morning and evening. After two months, I began to experience a number of changes.

"My CPR, an indicator of how rheumatism is progressing, fell from 1.8 to 1.1. My body temperature, which had been low on awaking each morning, gradually began to rise. The swelling in my fingers subsided. As a result, carrying things and wringing cloths has become a little easier."

- **Rheumatism #2 (47-year-old woman)**
  "At one time I took a lot of drugs for my stomach ulcers. Therefore, about six months ago, I suddenly experienced a swollen spleen. This led to my being diagnosed with a reduction in my white blood cell count and pancreatitis. My left side from my stomach to my spine was extremely painful, but all I could do was to avoid medication and rest. On the recommendation of a friend, I began to drink UFO mixed with energy water. Three days later, the pain went away, and my whole body felt lighter. However, on the second week, the pain reappeared. Attributing it to the improvement reaction, I continued drinking Pi-Water. At the fourth week, I felt a lot better than I had before I started drinking. I intend to go on drinking like this."

To continue drinking Pi-Water is the correct approach. When you first drink Pi-Water, the effect is dramatic. But when you continue for a while, you will experience a relapse. There is a tendency for many people to stop there, but this is the point from which it really begins to work and you should continue as before.

If you continue, even though we don't really know how, it will probably tackle the root cause of illnesses, even those for which there is no known cause. I believe this is why we can see examples of Pi-Water bringing about results that can only be termed "miraculous."

In the medical profession there are those who will not even try to recognize something that cannot be logically explained. However, what patients who are suffering require is a cure or something to alleviate their symptoms, not logic. Pi-Water itself does not act as a medicine. However, it certainly does provide the ideal water source for a living organism and thereby helps rejuvenate the body's physiological functions.

### IMPROVEMENT REACTION LIKENED TO BIRTH PAINS

When you fast, an interesting reaction occurs. If you have suffered previously from some illness, then similar symptoms will appear. For example, a person who has had stomach ulcers will experience symptoms similar to those of ulcers again. With various types of illness the same symptoms will recur as if a videotape were being replayed.

Moreover, if you are currently sick, then you will experience a temporary increase in your symptoms. Or, if there is an accumulation of toxic substances, you will experience fevers, eczema, runny nose, and other such symptoms aimed at expelling those substances. Why does this happen?

In order to understand this, I'd like you to think of the change of scenery that occurs when you do your spring cleaning. When you do your spring cleaning, in the end things look so clean that you don't recognize them. However, halfway through, things look such a mess that they would appear to be impossible to clean up. Often, when you try to fix something thoroughly, things seem to go in the opposite direction at first. In human terms, it is like a fight leading to a unique friendship.

When Pi-Water enters the human body, it would appear that is acts to correct the very fundamentals of our physical being. It is thought that it is this that leads to the improvement reaction, although the shape this takes will depend on the individual or his or her lifestyle, natural disposition, genetic characteristics, and so on. It will not always be the same.

Therefore, it is important not to be put off by the negative changes that soon occur in your body after beginning to drink high-energy Pi-Water for a while. It is important to be careful and watch your progress. Please refer to the following typical example of a personal experience of the improvement reaction:

- **Improvement reaction (53-year-old man)**
  "Before drinking Pi-Water, I had high blood pressure, a symptom of Meniere's disease. Dizziness and nausea were particularly bad. I even had to be picked up by ambulance when I went somewhere once. I would wake up in the middle of the night, my legs were so numb. I had to have electrical massage every day.

  "I began drinking energy water on the 20th of October. After five or six days my stomach was swollen and really painful. About one month later on the 18th of November, I began drinking UFO. The following is a record of the changes that occurred from the next day onward:

  *November*

  21: Entire face red. Nosebleed in the morning.
  22: As above.
  23: Same as above. Rash appeared on back after bath.
  24: Pain in left side chest during morning.
  25: As above.
  26: Rise in blood pressure. Took medicine to get pressure down.
  28: Nosebleed in evening.

  After all the above symptoms had appeared, they then completely disappeared and never returned. The numbness in the legs that accompanies Meniere's disease also went away in next to no time. Now, I don't need massage at all. I seem to be completely healthy."

This kind of improvement reaction often occurs with Pi-Water, but this just shows how much it is working on the basic life functions.

When an improvement occurs while fasting, people in the know rejoice. This is because it's like receiving a check for your health. With Pi-Water, too, when an odd reaction occurs on beginning to drink it, you can take it as a sign that your cells have begun to rejuvenate.

## CHANGING FLUID IN BODY HELPS ANEMIA

Red blood cells carry oxygen in the blood. It is these red blood cells that are responsible for conveying oxygen throughout the body. However, we develop anemia when there is a deficiency in these red blood cells, and they are unable to carry out their proper function. Oxygen can no longer be carried throughout the body. Therefore, an oxygen deficiency will occur in various parts of the body leading to different kinds of problems.

There are a number of causes of anemia: if you lose a lot of blood from an injury; if there is a deficiency in the iron that is so important to the red blood cells; or if there is a vitamin deficiency ($B_{12}$, folic acid). Also, there is a type of anemia that shortens the life of the red blood cells and another in which poor regeneration occurs because of deterioration in the body's blood-forming function.

Depending on the cause of the anemia, the treatment will vary, but usually the prescribed treatment will involve taking plenty of iron, vitamins, and protein. However, this kind of treatment is by no means comprehensive. That is to say, this is another kind of symptomatic treatment and, therefore, doesn't go to the very root of the problem that is causing these various deficiencies.

Just saying that there is a deficiency in iron or vitamins doesn't mean the problem has necessarily to do with the amount you are consuming. Even if the body has iron available, it is probably not in a position to use it. Thus, in order to bring about an improvement in anemia, it is important to improve the functions of the body as a whole. The following personal experiences show what kind of effect Pi-Water has on anemia:

- **Improvement in blood disorders #1 (45-year-old man)**
  "I have low hemoglobin in my blood. Moreover, electrocardiograms show an abnormality in my heartbeat. I had been feeling constantly out of condition. My wife attended a talk on Pi-Water and came back with a bottle of it. I began to

drink it and felt much better as a whole that I decided to continue taking it and installed an energy water purifier.

"To be honest, I didn't think for one moment that just by drinking water I would get healthier, but I continued to drink 1.5 liters per day. After a while, at a health checkup, I found that my hemoglobin was now 14.2, a good value. I was really surprised."

- **Improvement in blood disorders #2** (**47-year-old man**)
"Two years after beginning dialysis for kidney disease, I felt better than before. However, my blood pressure and anemia were still giving me problems. I heard about high-energy Pi-Water from an acquaintance and began drinking a few drops every day. About six months later, the black lines through my nails began to disappear, and the black discoloration around my navel also faded.

"My constipation disappeared, too, and my eczema receded, leaving my skin nice and clean. I went to see the doctor and it seems my anemia had shown a great improvement. I used to always have physical problems with this and that, but since beginning to drink UFO, all my previous complaints have improved and nothing has gotten worse."

- **Improvement in blood disorders #3** (**27-year-old man**)
"When I was 19, I was told I had aplastic anemia. I have been receiving treatment as an outpatient ever since. When I was admitted to the hospital for another problem, I contracted Hepatitis C through a blood transfusion. I had been on medication for anemia for some time. However, nothing had effected a basic cure. One day, my mother told me about Pi-Water, and she had the Pi-Water purifier installed for me.

"I took UFO along with energy water, and I even took a bottle with me whenever I went to work. I made sure to drink more than one liter of energy water every day. Around three months after I began drinking it, I went for a checkup at the hospital. They found my hemoglobin had returned to the normal value."

- **Improvement in blood disorders #4**
  A terminally ill cancer patient was given high-energy Pi-Water. One week later, it was found that his "red blood cells, which had been in a critical condition, had returned to the normal value" (report by Alfonso Won, Doctor of Natural Medicine in Canada). From this report and clinical examples it can be seen that Pi-Water works to normalize red cell values.

### IMPROVEMENT IN SYMPTOMS OF INCURABLE DISEASES

Despite the great advances made by medicine, there are still many diseases of which the cause is unknown and for which there is no treatment. If you are struck by such a disease, then your life will become very hard. If you go to a doctor, you will receive tests and medicine, but, even if you take those drugs, you may not be cured. Even if you manage to keep the symptoms under control, there is always the fear of side effects. Pi-Water can offer a little hope to such people. Let us have a look at three personal experiences:

- **Improvement in collagen disease (57-year-old woman)**
  "I was continually feeling under the weather, so I went to the doctor for a checkup. I was diagnosed as having a collagen disease and fibroid lung. I had no choice but to be hospitalized for two months. Collagen disease is a type of immune system problem, and it seems no one really knows the cause. Fibroid lung is an incurable disease in which the fibers in your lung tissue increase, causing difficulty in breathing. After two months in the hospital, I was still in a lot of pain every day. I was feeling really down. I was having to contend with two different incurable diseases and wondering how I was going to live the rest of my life. It was at this point that I was introduced to Pi-Water. I got the water purifier installed as soon as possible and began drinking energy water. The effect was amazing. My symptoms subsided. I did feel a lot better physically. But what really

made me happy was that I felt a lot more cheerful about myself."

Many people find that they feel happier after drinking Pi-Water. Even if the symptoms themselves don't show great improvement, feeling better within yourself will play an important role in heightening your own powers of self-healing. In this woman's case, she started to feel better. She really took to Pi-Water and started to use UFO as well.

She says that after that her body, which had been as hard as rock before, gradually started to soften up. She was finally able to get over the headaches and stiff shoulders that had plagued her for 30 years.

It is believed that the major factor in collagen disease is a psychological one. Often, when the victim's mental state alters in a positive way, he or she will see an improvement. Medicine can sometimes have a placebo effect: if the patient thinks, "This is really effective," then it may work, even if it's just a tablet of yeast.

How Pi-Water works to affect each individual disease is, as yet, unclear from a pharmacological point of view. However, it is a fact that it does have a definite effect on a number of incurable diseases that modern medicine has all but abandoned. We are doing our best to explain its mystery from a scientific and clinical standpoint. However, for the people who really need it, I believe it would be a waste to think, "I won't use it until its mystery is solved."

- **Improvement in incurable intestinal disease (55-year-old woman)**

"Twenty-five years ago I developed nephrocystosis and hepatic cysts. I underwent tests at a number of university hospitals. But they all told me it was incurable, and here I am today. My liver has hardened and enlarged and now hangs over my stomach. My kidneys, too, both of them, have hardened and enlarged to the size of a fist. I sometimes feel they are on fire, they are so painful.

"There is no treatment for my condition, so all I could do was to brew up and drink various medicinal herbs that were supposed to be good. Then, I started to use high-energy Pi-Water in conjunction with them on a daily basis. First, my body fat started to reduce, and then my body started to soften up a bit. The intense pain I had had after eating disappeared, and my complexion improved. I feel much better now than I ever have before."

- **Improvement in side effects from steroids (24-year-old woman)**

  "When I was 22, I was hospitalized for a month for ulcerous colitis. On leaving the hospital, I went to study abroad. Three months later, I suffered a relapse and had to be hospitalized once again. It was at this point that I was put on a health diet and a course of steroids. However, one year later, my condition worsened, and I had to return to the hospital.

  "If you take a lot of steroids, it seems you will soon see an improvement. But my white blood cell count fell by half, and I had the worry of being susceptible to a number of infectious diseases as a side effect of such treatment. I had reached the worrysome point where a pattern was emerging in which the symptoms would begin to appear around the spring and then worsen with the coming of summer. At this point I found out about Pi-Water. I still stuck to my diet and continued to drink Pi-Water at the same time. After only one month, I felt a lot better. As far as I'm concerned, I feel completely cured. I couldn't be happier."

# CHAPTER FIVE

❁ ❁ ❁

## HOW WIDE THE RANGE OF APPLICATIONS!

In Chapter Four, I referred to the effect of Pi-Water in a number of different health areas. I believe that you now know how widespread the effect of Pi-Water on illness to be. Of course, there are still many unexplained aspects of Pi-Water. But the fact that Pi-Water works to enhance life is certain.

## USE IN FARMING PRODUCES BOUNTIFUL AND SAFE CROPS

In this chapter, I would like to introduce to you a number of actual examples showing how widely Pi-Water demonstrates its hidden powers in a number of nonmedical fields. First, I would like to look at its use in the field of agriculture. In connection with the production of food, we now face two major problems. One concerns the worldwide shortage of food that continues even today. Among a world population of some six billion people, it is said that some one to two billion face starvation. Increasing the production of food is, therefore, a major concern.

So how much can Pi-Water contribute to solving this problem? The fact is that the agricultural chemicals and chemical fertilizers that have been used up to now to increase food production have brought with them a number of problems, not just pollution of our rivers and lakes and exhaustion of the land but also, as is widely known, the contamination of food itself.

Even with these problems, we are still faced with the imperative of increasing food production. Pi-Water, in addition to offering the possibility of increasing food production, can also contribute to cleaning up the environment. Thus, there is already proof that the effect of Pi-Water can be expected to accomplish two objectives at the same time.

How is Pi-Water being used in connection with agriculture? As an example, let's look at what it has done for rice production. Pi-Water is being tried out in two ways in the field of agriculture: as water and in Pi-converted materials for improving soil. In Ogata Village, Akita prefecture, Japan, researchers carried out the following experiment with energy water in rice farming:

1. Before growing the young rice plant, a certain type of seed (akitakomachi) was soaked in energy water for a period of 20 days. During this period, the water was changed five times.
2. In raising the young seedlings, researchers administered the energy water between seven to ten times.
3. After planting the seedlings, the researchers flooded the paddy with energy water a total of eight times during the cultivation period spanning May to the beginning of August.

Altogether, this used up a total of 800 tons of energy water. The same experiment was carried out in Toyama and Niigata prefectures, too. The results showed that the rice produced was of a higher quality than that produced with the usual type of water. It was also possible to increase the amount harvested by between 10 and 20 percent.

Another experiment involved a soil improvement agent AKANE. When the soil was treated with Pi, it showed almost the same results as that obtained with energy water. The following is the testimony of someone who tried such an agent in rice farming:

"First, the way the roots of the plants spread was completely different. Each root was fatter and longer. And a fine stubble was also produced. The roots reached deep down into the soil. The amount of nourishment they could get from the soil was completely different. They were also very strong and robust.

"Not just in rice, I'm also using it for vegetables. It has made raising organically grown vegetables much easier than before. For the rice fields, for soil improvement, for spraying the leaves, for making compost, and so on, I'm using between 60 to 70 kilograms per every 10 ares."

The fact is, Pi-Water has the power to rejuvenate the cells of any living thing. It has also been confirmed that by using Pi-Water in rice fields, large numbers of worms have appeared that had hitherto been unable to survive under modern farming methods. Moreover, Pi-Water's remarkable effect has been witnessed not just in rice farming but also over a wide range of other vegetable and plant produce such as pumpkins, potatoes, onions, cucumbers, tomatoes, eggplants, and so on.

The following example illustrates the use of Pi-Water in an agricultural undertaking:

- **Cultivation of salad vegetables** (**37-year-old man**)
  "When I found out about Pi-Water, I was involved in experiments cultivating salad vegetables at a vegetable producing facility. However, the vegetables would often turn brown around the edges. They had a peculiar grassy smell and bitter taste. They would have been unsatisfactory for the market. When I heard a talk on Pi-Water, I realized anew how important the role of water was in the growing of vegetables, so I got the Pi-Water Purifier installed as soon as possible.

  The following are the results of my using energy water in an experiment:

  1. The budding rate improved by between 80 to 100 percent.
  2. The plants were robust and less prone to disease.
  3. The color was better, and they were firm and fat. Size increased.
  4. The grassy smell disappeared, and they were sweeter.

  These were among the various improvements that occurred. We were finally able to produce the organically grown and delicious vegetables that we had hoped for."

I believe that nonchemically enhanced, organically produced food will be the biggest issue of the 21st century. On top of that, we must also ensure production in sufficient amounts. I am convinced that the use of Pi-Water in agriculture can solve this difficult problem, along with that of how to revive exhausted soil.

### USES IN HOME-GROWN VEGETABLES AND PLANTS

Pi-Water is effective in agricultural production, so, of course, it is also useful in raising plants at home, too. When energy water is used in nurseries and on bonsai trees, the color of vegetables and plants improves, and plants such as cyclamen will bloom twice a year. Moreover, if it is sprayed directly onto leaves, it will also act to keep away pests.

Again, when it is used in Ikebana flower arrangement and in hydroponics, it increases the life span of the plants and encourages them to grow vigorously. With Ikebana, if you cut the stems while they are in energy water and then leave them like that for between three to five minutes, they will remain open and fresher longer.

In producing home-grown vegetables raised from seeds, if you soak them in energy water overnight before sowing, not only will yield improve, but you won't believe the difference in the young seedlings. Let's look at a few examples in which people have used energy water to raise plants at home:

- **Use in cut flowers (34-year-old woman)**
  "I was astonished at the resulting harvest when I tried it with my cut flowers. Flowers like lilies and carnations that had just withered up to now without coming out bloomed beautifully. Furthermore, if I soaked tired vegetables for about 30 minutes, the leaves would freshened up."

- **Use in foliating plants (46- year-old woman)**
  "We have a lucky tree in our shop (a beauty salon), and we haven't given it any special compost or anything for three years now. All we give it is energy water. Despite that, not only does it continue to bloom fresh and green and give pleasure to our customers, but at the end of the year it buds and produces a little white flower."

- **Use in bonsai trees (52-year-old man)**
  "My hobby is cultivating bonsai trees. I spray them with energy water every day, and moss just naturally appears in

the surrounding soil. I believe this to be proof that the soil is alive. Without any great effort on my part, the value of my bonsai trees has rocketed. I feel I've gained a lot by it."

- **Prevention of soil mold in potted plants** (51-year-old woman)
  "I am in the habit of always giving my potted plants energy water every day at home. It has made quite a difference from the way they were when I just used ordinary water: they are a much fresher green and the blackish mold has disappeared from the surrounding soil. Recently, I soaked a rusted pair of pliers in energy water, and the rust just dropped away. Now I can use them again."

- **Use in flowering garden trees** (47-year-old man)
  "Both the two Sakura and three cherry trees we have at home had failed to bloom for the past five years. After we started using energy water on them, giving them some every three days, all of them flowered beautifully."

- **Prevention of leaves shedding** (42-year-old woman)
  "After giving energy water a try, the first thing I noticed was that they all looked much better than before. My trees looked better. My goldfish swam around and were much more lively than before. I felt better, too. Later, I received a cedar tree as a birthday present from a friend. The fact is, to be frank, cedar trees tend to shed their leaves so they weren't really my favorite. However, when I gave them energy water, I had no trouble with falling leaves at all."

When giving Pi-Water to plants, you should put plenty into a saucer so that the roots won't rot. In addition, if you verbally encourage them, saying, "Grow strong and happy," at the same time as giving them energy water, they will begin to revive before your eyes. I believe this to be a case of the energy of Pi-Water to enhance life working together with our own life force. In this way, our feelings are communicated to the plant.

### FRESHWATER AND SALTWATER FISH ABLE TO CO-EXIST

Extremely good results have also been obtained with energy water in the raising of fish. When keeping tropical fish in a tank, the quality of the water is a problem. If you leave the water as it is, it will oxidize and the pH level will fall. When this happens, the fish can easily fall ill. As with humans, with fish, too, oxidization is to be feared.

Having said that, if you just change the water, the pH level will suddenly rise and the fish will suffer from pH shock. pH shock occurs when the concentration of hydrogen ions in the water suddenly changes. If this happens, the outer cellular structure of the fish's body will be damaged.

Therefore, it is imperative to keep a close watch on the quality of water in an extremely confined water environment when raising fish in a fish tank. However, when you use energy water, the water stays cleaner. Perhaps because the environment does not deteriorate, the fish are thus much easier to raise.

According to people who have raised fish using energy water, the fish are clearly more resistant to illness. Their ability to lay eggs is also improved. Water plants, too, show improved growth. That is to say, without putting in any extra work, all the elements needed to provide a good environment in which the fish can grow will be improved.

As an extreme example of this, there is one case where freshwater and saltwater fish have been able to co-habit. One person has actually experimented with this. First, he put 300 grams of saltwater into 60 liters of energy water. He then put in some saltwater fish from Okinawa (cobalt-sparrow) and some varieties of goldfish. On observation, they were found to be co-existing quite happily.

In the world of nature there are sometimes circumstances in which saltwater and freshwater fish are able to share the same environment, but this has rarely been reported as an artificial experiment. Therefore, this enabling of the two varieties to co-exist would seem to suggest huge possibilities for energy water in the field of marine production.

Pi-Water has produced some landmark results in the field of marine production. At a center for breeding eels, tests were carried out on comparative growth rates among young specimens. Even when compared with those raised in subterranean water, usually considered to produce higher quality, those raised using Pi-Water showed growth rates of two to three times faster. Moreover, the taste of the adult fish was found to be of higher quality.

Even when fish are kept to be eaten fresh, if they are kept in Pi-Water, the water in the tank will maintain its quality and lack of oxygen can be avoided. It is said that even if you put larger amounts of fish into the tank, the quality of the fish, too, will improve.

According to one Japanese restaurant that started to keep its fish in Pi-Water, it had always been said that fish bred in captivity were not as tasty as those bred in the wild. However, after three to four days in a tank containing Pi-Water, the fish bred in captivity were in no way inferior in taste to those found in the wild.

There has been one comparative experiment conducted by energy water lovers on littleneck clams. The same amounts of both ordinary water and energy water were put into separate vessels, and natural salt was added to provide an environment close to that of saltwater. Fresh littleneck clams were then put into each tank. They were observed to see what changes might occur. The clams in the energy water soon put out their tubes and began to make a strong peeping noise in the air. However, those in the ordinary water kept their tubes retracted. When we put one spoonful of energy water into their tank, in no time at all a large number had extended their tubes, too.

I believe that this type of change takes place in humans and plant life alike. All life exists as a cellular structure and supports that life through its DNA. I believe that Pi-Water works to positively affect this common factor, the root of all life.

- **Example of recovery in sick goldfish (73-year-old man)**
  "My grandson came home with a goldfish (Ranchu) that had been discarded because it was sick. We didn't give it any food, but just let it stay in some energy water for a while and waited to see what would happen. It got a little better, so we decided to gradually increase its ration of food. When he first brought it back, almost half its tail fins had disappeared. However, about one year later, it had a beautiful set. The color was much better, too. It had turned into a lovely specimen to look at. I also think it's amazing we were able to raise it this far without an air pump."

### HEALING POWER IN PETS

In addition to the beneficial effect of Pi-Water on human health, its influence in pet care is also astonishing. The following is a summary of a personal description given us by Dr. Hisayuki Mototake who manages an animal hospital in Kumamoto:

"Male cats often suffer from blockage of the urinary tract. This leads to the bladder's swelling to the size of a human fist, way beyond its normal capacity. This is dangerous. Naturally, surgery is required. However, in one case on cleaning out the bladder with one part of high-energy Pi-Water (UFO) to 1000 parts Ringer's solution, the animal recovered within three days.

"I had a parakeet brought into the hospital, weak from being riddled with an external parasite (scabies), its bill and legs looking like a beehive. I rubbed pure oil (Pi-treated oil) into the affected areas, and the diseased areas just seemed to flake away. I applied two drops of high-energy Pi-Water locally, five times per day. On top of that, I gave the parakeet a mixture of high-energy Pi-Water and glucose through a syringe every 30 minutes. The bird made a full recovery on the second day.

"I treated one old dog that had suffered dizziness for 24 hours because of an abnormality in the three semicircular canals in its ear that control its sense of balance. I had not effected a cure for this problem before. But, I persevered and gave it high-energy Pi-Water five times per day, and it showed a remarkable improvement.

"I had one mongrel dog that showed a heavy build-up in its bowels during an X-ray. This is where the intestines have become entangled. Usually, this would require surgery. I injected energy water and UFO into the bowels and massaged the affected area with UFO. As a result, the dog recovered without surgery."

Dr. Mototake makes sure to use Pi-Water for a number of problems. It seems that high-energy Pi-Water has proved more effective than other medicines in treating both internal illnesses, such as infections, colitis, liver malfunction, and so on and also problems like broken bones and wounds.

In using Pi-Water to maintain the health of a pet, the most basic thing to do is give it as drinking water. If the pet, whether it be cat or dog, drinks energy water on a daily basis, its coat will shine and the smell of its stool will greatly improve.

They say that, in the absence of strict rules governing it, pet food contains large amounts of preservatives and additives. As a result, the animals' organs become exhausted trying to expel the harmful chemicals that are absorbed into the body. Recently, the number of pets showing the same type of symptoms displayed by humans with adult diseases has increased.

Accordingly, there is no problem in using energy water for pets in the same way you use it for humans or plants. In other words, you should use it in all the ways you would use normal water, not just as drinking water. If you do this, I believe you will be able to maintain the pet in good health because it will be in a hygienic environment.

"I get the impression that Pi-Water very precisely conveys information on how to recover as well as conveying the required energy to damaged cells. I believe that this conveying of both information and energy could be seen as energy water's greatest and most unique feature."

This is the conclusion reached by Dr. Mototake, a great advocate of Pi-Water. However, let us also look at Dr. Mototake's opinion as to why Pi-Water shows its healing effect far more markedly in humans than in animals.

"The reason why it works better in humans than in animals is that the former are aware of what they are drinking."

This is a rather important point. There is a clear difference in the effect of Pi-Water on those who drink it believing and those who drink it with doubt. Even so, you can explain the benefits of Pi-Water to a human being while you cannot to an animal. In order to use it effectively with animals, it is important to be as loving as possible toward that animal and endeavor to gain its trust.

The following experiences show how Pi-Water helps pets:

- **Pet Cured #1 (44-year-old man)**

  "I run a beauty salon for pets. My family and I love dogs very much, and we have some 30 of them at home. We love all of them. One day our six-year-old Maltese fell down the stairs and critically injured himself. I immediately gave him a heart massage, but his whole body was convulsing and his breathing was very faint. It didn't look like as if he would recover.

  "I had to do something, so I took him to a vet who was supposed to be very good. The pressure on the dog's brain was intense, as he had hit his head hard in the fall. A blood test showed his blood sugar to be low and his liver damaged. We were told that there was nothing to be done. So the vet patched him up as best he could, and we took him home. I, too, gave up thinking there was anything we could do.

  "At that point, a customer of mine brought me some energy water and UFO. I immediately tried getting the dog to drink some. He had been just able to totter about until then, but after that he got even worse, day by day. Finally, all he could do was snore away, fast asleep. Just when I felt that this time I would have to prepare for the worst, a miracle occurred on the third day. On awaking, he showed an appetite. His eyes were shining, and for the first time in many days, he was able to tell me what he wanted with a bright and cheery bark. I kept on giving him energy water and UFO after that. He is still alive and happy as a member of our family."

- **Pet Cured #2 (40-year-old woman)**
  "I remember, one rainy day, I ran across a skinny little Maltese puppy in the street. I felt sorry for it and took it home. However, its urine was a dark brownish color, and I took it to the vet to be looked at. It seems it had a weak liver and kidneys. This was just after I'd had the Pi-Water Purifier installed, so I immediately started to give it energy water to drink. Three months later, its urine became clear, its coat regained its shine, and the mucus cleared up from its eyes."

### POWERFUL TOOL IN INCREASING PROFITS IN HUSBANDRY

Energy water and Pi-Water are also widely used in the field of husbandry. They are powerful weapons in the fight to increase profits and improve management efficiency. For example, it has improved the egg-laying rate in chickens. The standard egg-laying period of a chicken is calculated to be 400 days.

When this period is exceeded, the egg-laying rate drops drastically, and the only thing the chicken is good for is consumption. However, if you give chickens energy water and Pi-treated food from the time they are chicks, they can continue to produce eggs even beyond this period. There is even one astounding example of a chicken continuing to produce for up to 900 days.

Moreover, the taste of the eggs is good, and the yolk of cracked eggs is so firm it can be held between the fingers. In China they say that for every egg you eat, you live a year longer. That is how nutritious eggs are: the perfect form of nourishment as a food. However, recently, eggs have changed:

that is because they now contain antibiotic substances because they are raised in an unnatural factory environment. These days, not only chicken farmers but also other stock farm producers, such as beef and pork farmers, face the same kind of problem as those producing crops using large amounts of agricultural chemicals and fertilizers.

Stock farmers using Pi-Water have completely solved the problems faced by the rest of the industry and are able to produce safe, high quality products. Using Pi-Water has also allowed them to improve their management and increase profits. Let's look at the following example of a producer (Sakai Stock Produce) using Pi-Water in their operations in Gunma prefecture.

The producer manages their herd of black-haired Japanese cows there by having neighboring farmers raise them. Nonetheless, they still fatten up a few head of cattle on their own farm. The company president, Mr. Kouichi Sakai, had just had Pi-Water equipment installed at home, so he decided to let the cattle drink it, too.

When they did this, the fattening process improved. It seemed that, by the time they were ready to be sold, Pi-Water had increased the average weight from 700 kilograms to specimens as heavy as 800 to 1,000 kilograms. Moreover, the quality of the meat also improved. In a ranking system of 1 to 5, with 5 as the highest, the ratio of produce being awarded a 4 or a 5 also increased. Realizing that this would clearly improve production, Mr. Sakai introduced energy water into the animal feed and supplied the cowsheds as part of a general management policy.

Interestingly, marbled beef is difficult to produce. It is considered to be high quality, and being unable to produce it is a minus for any livestock farmer. However, Mr. Sakai felt that, "marbled beef indicates the presence of buildup of cholesterol in the body and is a sickness similar to diabetes. Therefore, Pi-Water, which works to promote life, would probably work against this process." This is correct.

Certainly, marbled beef probably tastes good. However, if you consider that cholesterol is a trigger for various adult diseases, you probably shouldn't risk eating such meat. If it were just a case of meat tasting bad if you couldn't produce marbled beef, then there would be no point in using Pi-Water.

Beef produced using Pi-Water contains an appropriate amount of fat. It is a matter of preference, but as far as taste goes, meat raised on energy water is just as delicious as marbled beef. The taste is good, there is no health problem, and it can be efficiently produced. Therefore, I believe that introducing Pi-Water to such farming would be a big plus.

There is another big problem affecting livestock production: the foul smells. This is a kind of environmental pollution. When you use Pi-Water, this foul odor will decrease. Fermentation will take precedence over putrefaction, and, therefore, hygiene will be improved. The percentage of livestock being affected by illness will also decrease.

Pigs raised in a production system that utilizes Pi-Water for drinking water and in feed produce meat between one to two ranks higher in quality. Not only that, but as the number affected by illness decreases, yield improves. From this point of view, too, there is no doubt that Pi-Water contributes to increasing profits.

### PI-SALT: THE IDEAL SALT THAT CONTRIBUTES TO HEALTH AND BEAUTY

As I have already described, water delivered to the body through the ferric ferrous salts in Pi-Water has the ability to enhance the various natural powers of the living organism. The reason for this is that Pi-Water has a connection to iron and salt. Pi-salt is made by Pi-treating natural salt, salt that contains microquantities of important elements found in abundance in natural saltwater. Therefore, it has a number of special qualities that other salts don't have.

Salt is an indispensable nutrient for human beings. It is connected to the action of the cells in the living organism, and if there is a deficit, the body can no longer function. It is thought that the word we now use for *salary* originally came from the word for *salt*. This shows how, in the past, salt was considered a thing of value, just as money is today.

However, these days, we are able to obtain as much salt as we like through various scientific methods, so there is no difficulty associated with finding it. It is dealt with casually as a cheap and basic foodstuff. The overconsumption of salt is regarded as a problem, and it is even sometimes thought to be the enemy of health.

However, modern chemically-produced salt has now become a substance containing more than over 99 percent sodium chloride and is something completely different from that which used to be considered of such high value. Naturally, the ideal salt is still obtainable from unpolluted saltwater. This kind of salt contains dozens of kinds of microscopic amounts of various other minerals in addition to sodium chloride.

Pi-salt is based on natural salt and is produced using a special and lengthy process. Therefore, it contains the same energy as Pi-Water. Of course, it also contains more than 20 types of those minerals found in microscopic quantities in saltwater, so as a salt readily available for consumption, I think it would be no exaggeration to say it is the ideal salt.

For example, it contains, iron, calcium, manganese, molybdenum, selenium, potassium, and others. Moreover, more than 50 percent of these elements have been ionized. This means that they have been revitalized and that when they are absorbed the body will accept them without any resistance.

Naturally, it is ideal for use in the home for cooking, for example, in pickling plums and scallions. When used in this way, the food keeps its nutritious value while its taste is improved. Pi-salt is often used in the preparation of miso, soybean paste, and soy sauce bases. Used in this way, you can expect it to have the same effect on your body as you would obtain through using Pi-Water, that is to say, the Pi-effect. It is said that too much salt may be harmful, but this applies to chemically-produced salt. Real salt, on the contrary, is very good for your health.

Not only is too much chemically-produced salt a problem, but also excessive amounts of sugar, alcohol, and tobacco can be unhealthful. In the case of chemically- produced salt, below ten grams is recommended as the ideal amount, but if you use Pi-salt, then there is no need to worry about the amount.

Moreover, the quality of such salt is good, so making homemade preserves is easier. For example, you should try making miso base (a stock), an essential in every household, using Pi-salt. If you have soybeans, malt, and Pi-salt, you should be able to make a first-class miso base, even if you've never tried it before. Any bookshop should have books on how to make miso base. Therefore, all you have to do is buy one and follow the recipe. Also, if you use Pi-salt, you will be able to make excellent homemade pickles, too, something that seems to be a dying art these days.

The same can be done with plum, scallions, and other foods. Some people feel that cooks who no longer make homemade pickles are lazy, but there's more to it than that. One big problem is that it is not possible to make good pickles using chemically-produced salt. Recently, the natural product has become readily available.

However, beware of "fake" salt that is no more than just sodium chloride with bittern and various types of minerals added. Using that type of salt, it is difficult to make salt processed goods. Pi-salt is a pure salt made from saltwater based on the formation of salt in ancient seawater, which is then further treated with Pi.

## PI-WATER AS A COOKING INGREDIENT

The following are some personal experience examples of how useful Pi-Water is in home cooking. It has many different uses in home cooking, and it can also be easily used for soaking foods.

- **Improving cooking (45-year-old woman)**
  "I now use Pi-Water in cooking, and my children say 'Our mum's cooking is much better than before!' I use it as cooking water, and I also soak ingredients in it. I feel that this brings out the natural flavor of the food. Also, I feel that food thus prepared cooks better."
- **Using in meat, sashimi, and dried fish (48-year-old woman)**
  "When I cook with Pi-Water, it gets rid of the small bruising in vegetables, and they get their freshness back. Let me tell you about one trick I use: I soak sirloin steak in Pi-Water. After it has been cleaned, I put it in hot water. After that, when I boil it, it becomes nice and tender. I soak leftover sashimi in Pi-Water for about 30 minutes and then pickle it in soy sauce. Two or three days later it tastes just as good as if it were fresh. With dried herrings too, if you cook them after soaking them for about 30 minutes, it takes away the fishy smell, and they taste better."
- **Making meat taste better (33-year-old woman)**
  "One day I had the idea of trying to soak meat in energy water. Without doing anything else, it really cleaned up the meat. I had no idea meat was that dirty. Since then, I have always made a point of soaking meat in energy water before cooking it. Now it doesn't smell bad anymore, it's more tender, and it tastes better."
- **Keeping fish in freezer for more than one year (73-year-old man)**
  "I caught some sardines with the aim of drying them. I prepared them in energy water. I found that even if they were kept frozen for a long time, when you defrosted them, they still tasted good."
- **Making old rice taste as good as new rice (35-year-old woman)**
  "Rice, even the very best brands, gets old and dry when it is

past its season. We are really fussy about the taste of our rice. When the season is over, we pay for expensive organically produced rice. One day, I tried preparing old rice washed in Pi-Water. I was amazed to find it tasted no different from new rice. Since then, we have been eating this transformed tasty 'new' rice."

- **Six tips for using energy water (43-year-old woman)**
  "Since I started using energy water, working in the kitchen has become much more fun. That's because my hobby now is finding all sorts of different ways to use Pi-Water with food. The following are some examples of the tricks I have come up with:
  1. Soaking fruit in energy water. The surface blemishes (agricultural chemicals?) just fall away. It tastes better, and it's safe.
  2. Soaking vegetables. We can keep them for a week, whereas before they only lasted two or three days.
  3. Soaking meat and fish. It takes away the smell, and even cheap meat tastes a notch up in quality.
  4. Putting a little energy water in soy sauce. It makes it a little smoother and takes away the sourness.
  5. Making coffee. Even though it gives coffee more body, the taste is still smooth and the smell good.
  6. Preparing rice. It makes rice with a perfect consistency."

As you can see from the above, there are a number of ways you can use energy water in cooking. Furthermore, if you use it to make miso soup, you can cut down a little on the amount of miso base you use without affecting the flavor. If you use energy water in soups it will improve the flavor of the ingredients by really bringing out the taste of the stock.

Maybe this is because of the influence of the clusters in the energy water. Solubility will be increased, and this will give your soup the true taste that will arise from the proper mixing of the ingredients. If you prepare soba and udon noodles and types of pasta such as spaghetti and ramen using energy water, they will assimilate heat better and come out with just the right texture.

Anybody can use energy water to make rice. And there are an overwhelming number of reports of its turning ordinary rice into high-class rice. The trick to making good tasting rice is using energy water at the very first stage when you wash the rice to prepare for cooking. Rice is extremely sensitive to the quality of the water it first comes into contact with. Therefore, if you wash it in ordinary tap water, even if you actually cook it in energy water, the effect will be halved.

If you use energy water to boil eggs, the shells won't break allowing the contents to spill out. They will also be easier to peel. When you use energy water in the preparation, it is also easier to remove the harshness taste in such vegetables as burdock, bamboo shoots, bracken, and fern. If you soak raw vegetables in energy water for 20 to 30 minutes and then prepare them, they will retain their freshness better than they will with ordinary water.

### YET MORE USES IN THE KITCHEN

When you use energy water in the kitchen, all your worries about food contamination and hygiene can be solved in an interesting way. The following show examples of how energy water can be used in the kitchen based on reports that have been sent into us.

#### *Cups, pots, pans, utensils*

If you soak tea-stained cups and scorched pans in energy water overnight, you won't recognize them, they'll be so clean the next day. Again, after you finish using utensils, soak them in energy water before you wash them, and they'll come clean, even if you don't use a lot of washing liquid.

#### *Cutting boards, dishtowels, cloths*

It is especially important to be careful with cutting boards from the point of view of hygiene. However, if you wash them in energy water, it will be difficult for mold and dirt to stick to them. With dishtowels and cloths, too, if you soak them in energy water, it will remove that embedded dirt in the material and will prevent them from smelling sour.

***Cooking suggestions***

When you use energy water, it not only brings out the flavor of the food and makes it more tender but also speeds up the process. It will make the flavor of the food milder. Soy beans and black soybeans will have a nicer color and will cook more quickly and turn out more tender than with ordinary water.

*Shellfish soups*

Asari, Shijimi, Hamaguri, and other types of clam usually tend to shrink on cooking. However, if you cook them after soaking them in energy water, they will taste better and not shrink so much.

*Draining the blood from meat and organs*

If you drain the blood from meat, liver, and giblets by soaking them for about 30 minutes in energy water, it will eliminate the smell and improve the flavor. They will also stay fresh longer. When you soak them, the color will change, but this is not particularly a problem. Soaking in Pi-Water will get rid of the bitterness peculiar to salmon roe, cod roe, and others, giving them a nice mellow flavor.

*Preserving fish and shellfish*

Energy water is great for preventing oxidization. Therefore, it is effective to put fish and shellfish in a vinyl bag and freeze them to preserve after washing them well in energy water. You should wash each fish well, after gutting it first. Sliced fish and shucked shellfish, too, should first be washed in energy water once before preserving. This way they will keep their freshness.

*Soaking tofu, soybean curd*

Put some tofu to soak in a container with energy water. If you change the water about once a day, it will keep its original freshness for up to three or four days. In fact, this will actually improve the flavor of the tofu.

*Eliminating worries about pollution from agricultural chemicals #1 (40-year-old woman)*
"Recently we have begun to see vegetables grown without chemicals and organically produced food in the shops. However, for us, the consumer, it's difficult to know which is the genuine article. But after stocking up on energy water, I was able to eat vegetables and fruit after soaking them. That way, I could be sure they were safe from pollution. I used to be scared of eating strawberries, but if I soak them for about 20 minutes, it really brings out the sweetness, and they taste great."

*Eliminating worries about pollution from agricultural chemicals #2 (62-year-old woman)*
"What pleased me most after getting energy water was being able to eat bananas, which I love, without any worry. If you soak fruit and vegetables in energy water for a few hours, the chemicals just come away in the water, making the water dirty. Now, I always do this with any fruit or vegetables that I eat raw. Any food that can be soaked in water, I soak in energy water."

### USEFUL PI-WATER PRODUCTS FOR THE HOME

#### *Pi-Water bath lotion (Pi-Time)*

Pi-Water bath lotion (Pi-Time) is a liquid bath lotion with a fermented rice extract base. If you put this in the water when you take a bath, not only will it make the water nice and soft, but it will also prevent your getting that chilly feeling you sometimes get after you get out of the bath. It is effective in alleviating tiredness, chills, stiff shoulders, and sore skin. It is also effective against atopic dermatitis, so you can sometimes get the improvement reaction just by using this alone. The following personal experiences illustrate these uses:

- **Pi-Time #1 (50-year-old woman)**
  "My husband hates the smell of chlorinated water, so we always make a point of using bath lotions. One day a friend recommended Pi-Time, so I gave it a try. I have a tendency toward chills, but I found it warmed me right through. Now, I can't do without it. My husband, who is really fussy about the smell of hot water, was delighted, too. The entire family looks forward to bathtime with Pi-Time.
  "Moreover, two or three days after we started using it, I had a second happy surprise when I noticed that the bathtub was no longer scaled up. Any dirt would come off just by pouring some water over it. I don't need a scrubbing brush any more."

- **Pi-Time #2 (19-year-old woman)**
  "For three years I have been plagued with atopic dermatitis. However, on the recommendation of my mother I started to use high-energy Pi-Water and Pi-Time. Today, three months later, my dermatitis has completely disappeared. I'm so happy; I've regained the lovely shiny skin I used to have."

***Aura transmitter (The Healer)***
The Healer is an infrared radiating style device. However, it is different from the usual type of infrared panel heater. At its core, it contains Pi-treated materials that have been incorporated into its ceramic panels. It is believed that Pi-treated ceramics have the ability to absorb and then radiate cosmic energy. It is also thought that this ability has the potential for use through media other than water. Actual experiments with the Pi-treated Healer has shown the infrared wave lengths it produces harmonize better with those of the body, allowing the body to be warmed up better, right to the core, compared with other heaters. It emits a very gentle heat, and there is no sharpness to the stimulation that it gives out. If you check the actual temperature of the room itself, it will not be so high.

The Healer (aura transmitter)

However, I think it's because you are being properly warmed to your core that you don't actually feel the cold. Moreover, the Healer was developed as an aura transmitter; it was not developed as a heater as such. Nevertheless, it appears to alleviate the pain from stiff shoulders and rheumatism and prevent the occurrence of asthma attacks.

***Kitchen garbage disposal unit (Pi-Cycle)***

In both the city and the countryside, households face the problem of how to dispose of their kitchen garbage. If you go to an electrical goods shop, you will find a number of garbage disposal products for sale. However, one type will work by electrically heat-drying the garbage; another will utilize microbes to break down the garbage. Somehow, none of them seems to be perfect. For example, it appears to be common for this second type to give off a bad smell at the stage where fermentation sets in.

The Pi-Cycle is of this second type. However, as it uses Pi-treated microbes, there is hardly any smell at all: the garbage turns into water and carbon dioxide and disappears. I believe

Pi-Cycle (kitchen garbage disposal unit)

that in terms of volume the garbage will be reduced to probably about one hundredth of its original volume. Even fishbones will disappear without trace within two to three hours. Needless to say, all that will remain will be minerals providing the perfect material for compost. Moreover, having seen a dog eat this final product with relish, it looks as if it may have even turned into good animal feed. Whatever the case, I am convinced that the Pi-Cycle is the finest product of its kind on the market today.

### POWER OF PI IN MANUFACTURING

Pi-Water also holds huge potential in the field of manufacturing. I talked about a number of examples of its application in the field of manufacturing in my previous book, *The Miracle of Pi-Water* (original Japanese version published by Kousaido). However, since then, I have learned of its being applied even more widely than before.

Kouta, in Aichi prefecture, is home to Tomiyasu Bisou, a company that specializes in shop design. The president of that company is Mr. Kiyoshi Tomiyasu. He is involved in designing many inventions that make use of Pi-Water, and I would like to introduce a few of those in particular that make unique use of Pi-Water.

First, let's look at the Pi-Block. These days, the concrete block is an indispensable material in the construction industry. In using cement as a building material, however, there are a number of problems that arise. In my previous book, I mentioned how Pi-Water can increase the strength of cement and also prevent cracking. Nevertheless, as long as we continue to use cement as a building material, we will run into problems of environmental pollution.

Mr Tomiyasu has designed a Pi-Block that doesn't require cement. Instead, it makes use of Pi-treated natural earth. It boasts greater strength than concrete and also has the ability to adjust itself according to the degree of humidity, in the same way that lumber does. It is a landmark invention. There is a fish tank situated in front of the offices of Tomiyasu Bisou. In it has been placed a Pi-Block around which numerous goldfish can be seen to be swimming happily. If this were an ordinary concrete block, there is no way goldfish could live in there. Furthermore, the basic material out of which it is constructed is earth, so even when it weathers after many years, it will just return to the soil, causing no environmental damage.

Mr. Tomiyasu has also designed a new type of so-called 24-hour bath that will not get moldy. This type of 24-hour bath had become popular, but there is a tendency for it to acquire unwanted bacteria in the process of the water being constantly recirculated. This has meant a sudden drop in consumer interest. However, by using Pi-Water, this problem disappears.

Something that holds out great hope for the future is an experiment in which a certain Pi-treated part is fitted to a diesel engine. The results show a huge improvement in the engine fuel consumption efficiency rating. If Pi-Water can improve the energy consumption efficiency of the motor vehicle, then it will have a new role to play in the solution of the world's energy problem.

The application of and knowledge about the phenomenon of Pi-Water have taken precedence over basic research. It could be said that we have only just begun, as far as basic research goes. However, I am convinced that research about Pi-Water will offer a powerful tool in solving the various problems currently faced by scientific technology.

# WORDS OF RECOMMENDATION

### SOLVING THE MYSTERY OF PI-WATER

Over many years, the creator of Pi-Water, Shouji Yamashita, carried out basic research into its properties. Through this research, he developed a daring new hypothesis: that the phytosin responsible for the control of the flowering phenomenon in plants (the process whereby a plant produces seeds on flowering) has more than one role. Not only does it merely control this seed-producing process, but it also accurately recognizes its own environment and decides its own growth pattern. This is the life-force phenomenon. In other words, it guides its own life force.

This phytosin consists of an iron compound (ferric ferrous salts) plus neutral fat. This combination, then, for the first time, could be said to have the potential to promote a specific reaction based on the basic substance of water.

So, to see whether this solution, named Pi-Water, constitutes the essence of the life phenomenon, the phenomenon of harmonization, Dr. Yamashita conducted a number of experiments: he put plant tissue in various solutions containing microscopic concentrations (approximately $10^{-12}$) of neutral fat and observed the outcome.

The result was that he was able to isolate a particular solution in which the petals and leaves showed no deterioration, even over a long period of time: the harmonization phenomenon.

What was of particular interest was that, when using this liquid, it became clear that not only plant tissue but also animal tissue showed no deterioration. This fact has often been reconfirmed under experimental conditions. On further investigation into this mechanism, Yamashita concluded that both plant life and animal life share a common principle.

An experiment utilizing the harmonizing Pi-Water based on the earlier experiments described above has also been carried out. This was begun on October 30th, 1970. White mouse muscle tissue was placed and left to rest in a glass beaker containing the harmonization liquid described above.

Some air pressure was left in the jar, and the jar was sealed at normal temperature.

Tissue left in a beaker containing only distilled water as a control began to show signs of deterioration after one week. Microbes proliferated rapidly causing the liquid to cloud. The tissue in the harmonizing Pi-Water, however, showed no signs of deterioration whatsoever. The liquid was still as clear as it had been in the beginning and showed no sign of clouding for some 14 years. The same experiment has been repeated by veterinary doctors using cat ovaries and has yielded the same result.

Needless to say, the length of existence of an organism is inseparably tied to its environment. In the normal sphere of animal life, it is supposed that this is the immediate physical environment with which a living organism comes into contact.

To illustrate this point, there is an experiment of particular interest. A pimento was soaked for 30 minutes in harmonizing Pi-Water and then sealed into a vinyl bag, kept at a temperature of 30 degrees Celsius, and left to rest in a cultivation room with normal sunlight. When it was compared with the control after two weeks, the following was found: the control showed tissue deterioration and a marked proliferation of microbes. The experimental material, however, showed that it had maintained its freshness until it ripened 30 days later. Moreover, it was ascertained that the control completely rotted during this same time period.

This shows that Pi-treated fruit keeps its freshness over a longer period of time. It also shows that it promotes the ripening of fruit in a bag. Not only was the sealed fruit affected but also the water in the bag: the entire so-called sphere of living organisms, including gases, was seen to be working toward the rejuvenation of the actual fruit itself.

In other words, Pi-Water works together with organic bodies to affect the whole environment in which that organism exists. It would be no mistake to think of it as formulating the very foundation on which life can be formed.

The organic and the physical world are not completely isolated from one another. There is a concept that physical matter, too, is a living thing (Shigeo Nozawa, recipient of the 1995 Science and Technology Agency Prize), that the life phenomenon and physical matter are not isolated phenomena. They are related in a way similar to the relationship between particles and wave motion in quantum theory where each works as a supplement for the other. However, setting this aside, looking at the results of the basic research conducted by Yamashita over many years, I would like you to take into consideration his idea that the true phenomenon of life is probably something beyond those physical changes taking place at the molecular level as found in standard physiochemical science.

I believe that Pi-Water is, therefore, the basis for the wide range of effects that we have observed in the fields of medicine, agriculture, and engineering. This book is a record of how Pi-Water theory has been applied to and has contributed to the development of medical science.

DR. NOBORU IIJIMA
EMERITUS PROFESSOR
ST. MARIANNA UNIVERSITY SCHOOL OF MEDICINE

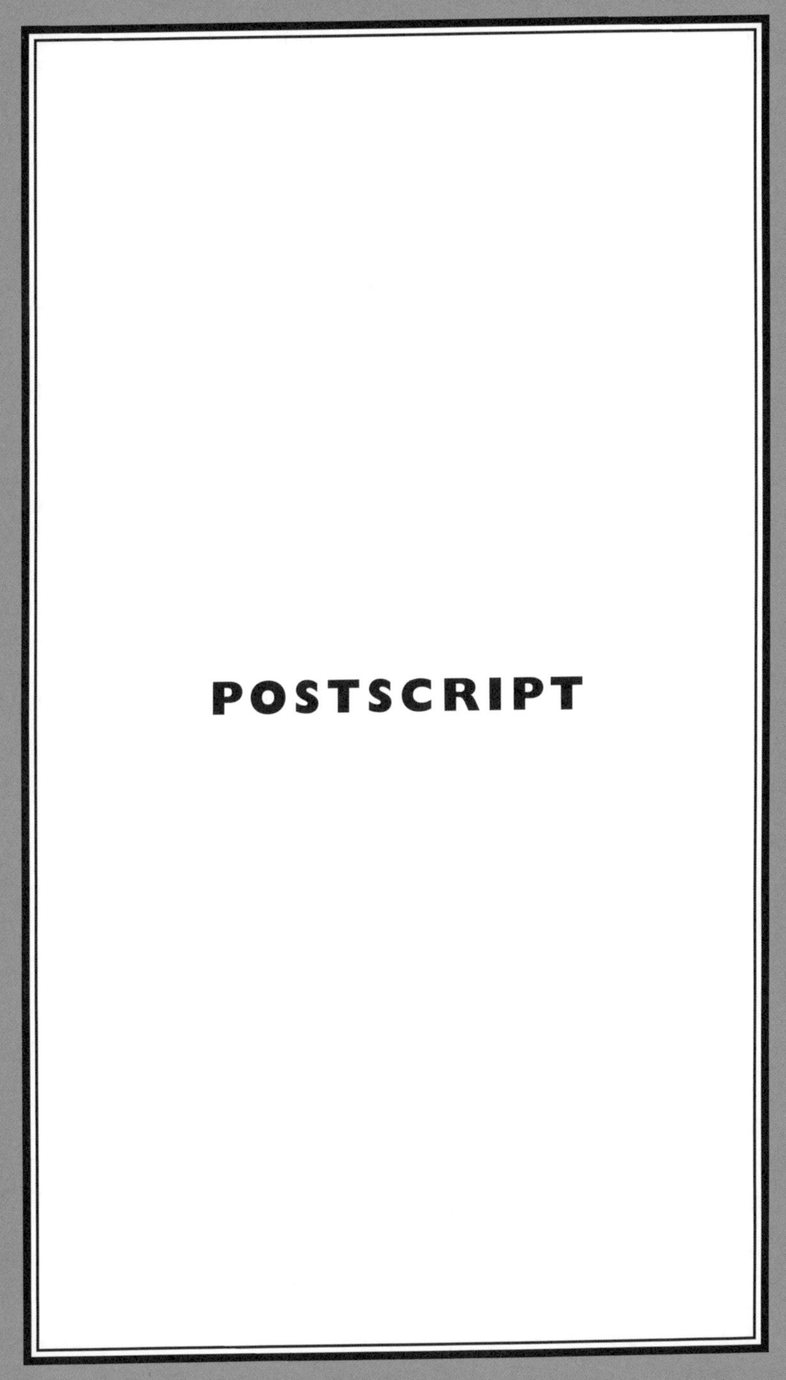

# POSTSCRIPT

Since the publication of my previous book, *The Miracle of Pi-Water*, the level of technology of Pi-Water systems has made great strides. It has been applied and put to practical use in a number of fields, beginning with those of medicine and health, then those of agriculture, fisheries, livestock farming, water pollution treatment, garbage disposal, waste gas purification, and so on. The number of fields to which it has been applied is extremely large. However, this time I have chosen to focus in particular on its application in the field of health care.

In the field of medicine and health, its application has clearly made much progress. Much of this has been made possible by the research contribution of the Association for Research and Propagation of Bio Energy Systems (Chairman, Iijima Noboru, Emeritus Professor, School of Medicine, St Marianna University). We have been able to reach this point thanks to the efforts of many medical professionals and doctors. To them, I would like to offer my deepest gratitude.

I would have liked to write in even greater detail about the problems in fields other than those of medicine and health. However, fearing that this would distort the focus of this current book, I decided to postpone that idea for the moment.

I hope that this book will provide a practical guide for those people concerned with and suffering from the those problems found in the various fields of medicine and health.

I would also like to offer my particular thanks to Satoko Itahashi of Kousaidou Publishing for her guidance, great encouragement, and patience in waiting for me to finish this manuscript.

September, 1998
Shinji Makino

Please address requests for further information and material on Pi-Water to the address below.

**The Association for Research and Propagation of Bio Energy Systems**
**The Secretariat**
486-7 Kawakami-cho, Totsuka Ward, Yokohama City,
Kanagawa Prefecture 244-0805
TEL. 81-45-826-0029 FAX. 81-45-825-1040